Male Red-bellied Paradise Flycatcher *Terpsiphone rufiventer*.
All photographs by the author.

BIRDS OF THE GAMBIA

An annotated check-list

by

M. E. J. GORE

B.O.U. Check-list No. 3 (2nd Revised Edition)

British Ornithologists' Union, 1990
c/o Zoological Museum, Tring, Herts HP23 6AP, UK

Second (revised) edition 1990

ISBN 0 907446 02 7

Printed in Great Britain by Henry Ling Ltd., at the Dorset Press, Dorchester, Dorset

CONTENTS

EDITOR'S FOREWORD (FIRST EDITION)

This is the third in the series of annotated check-lists being published by the British Ornithologists' Union and follows the same pattern and systematic treatment as its predecessors for Libya (1976) and Zanzibar and Pemba (1979). The Gambia is no exception to the general rule that national boundaries do not coincide with zoogeographical divisions, though it is closely related to and dependent on the Gambia River throughout; and it is to be emphasised that the check-list should be read preferably in conjunction with the literature of Senegal in particular G. J. Morel's *Liste Commentée des Oiseaux du Sénégal et de la Gambie*.

The Gambia, like other West and East African countries, is opening its doors to more tourism, with the likelihood of two usual developments. First, the disturbance of natural habitats as a result of at least coastal areas being opened up for commercial leisure pursuits; and secondly, an increase in ornithological observations. In addition, changing patterns of agriculture and national developments are likely to produce marked changes in the next decade. For these reasons, a basis for judging the effects of these factors on the Gambian environment is valuable at this stage.

It is to be hoped that visitors will inform the author or the editor of contradictions, confirmations and additions to the present analysis for any future revision.

J. F. Monk

SECOND (REVISED) EDITION

This is the first of the successful check-list series to be revised and published by the British Ornithologists' Union. As The Gambia is an enclave of Senegal, the revision complements the recent literature of Senegal.

Sadly but understandably, during the last decade, the Jakhaly swamp has been drained for agricultural purposes and woodland on the south bank depleted. Such pressures will continue and probably increase. Tourism is now well established and more and more ornithologists are discovering the excitement of African ornithology. Their observations have been invaluable in updating the material for this new edition. Future visitors are encouraged to send their data to either the author or the Gambian Ornithological Society.

L. G. Grimes

PREFACE TO THE SECOND (REVISED) EDITION

Birds of the Gambia, the third in the BOU Check-list series and published in 1981, went out of print more than three years ago largely as a result of the demand for copies by European bird-watchers who have been visiting The Gambia in increasing numbers in recent years.

The 1981 edition contained all records up to the end of 1979. Since then 18 species have been added to the Gambian list, the status of several species has been updated because new information has become available, the range of some species has expanded and retracted in others, and new breeding data has become available.

It is appropriate, therefore, to produce a completely revised edition. This contains records to the beginning of 1990 thus adding a little more than 10 years information to the published work on the birds of The Gambia. I have retained the format of the 1981 edition and much of the contents of the introductory sections remains unchanged, merely being up-dated as appropriate. For convenience I have slightly amended the division of the Gambia River, described as Lower, Middle and Upper River (see page 32), and I have included a Gazetteer under each section of the river to enable readers more easily to locate townships and villages referred to in the text.

A major innovation is the inclusion of a set of colour photographs in addition to the black and white photographs, depicting species typical of the various types of habitat in The Gambia.

British Embassy
Monrovia
Liberia

M. E. J. Gore
31 March 1990

The British Ornithologists' Union
is grateful to

Shell Marketing Gambia Ltd

for their contribution towards the cost
of producing the colour plates

List of Figures

List of Species Illustrated

Black and White Plates

Colour Plates

INTRODUCTION

The Gambia, formerly a British colony and since 1965 an independent country within the Commonwealth, comprises a narrow strip of land averaging only 25 km wide on either side of the River Gambia at latitude 13° N on the West African coast. Because of its geographical position, bordering one of the great rivers of Africa in an area which is generally arid, The Gambia has a much larger avian fauna, both in the number of species which occur and in the density of birds, than might normally be expected in a country which covers just 10,000 square kilometres.

The only town of any size is the capital, Banjul (formerly Bathurst), which is situated at the mouth of the river (Fig. 1). It is here and in the residential suburb of Fajara 10 miles away on the Atlantic coast, which is also the centre for tourists, that most of those interested in birds have lived. It is inevitable, therefore, that while the birds of the coast and Lower River region are fairly well known, less is known about the status of those further inland, particularly away from the river.

Sadly, an exceptional inland habitat, Jakhaly swamp 270 km up-river (Fig. 2), well watched in the 1970s when it comprised an extensive area of marshes, infested with warthogs, has now been drained. Formerly large numbers of waterfowl and waders concentrated there during the dry season when other freshwater marshes in the region dried up. Elsewhere inland, the woodland on the south bank, much depleted in the past 10 years, and the savanna along most of the north bank have been rarely visited.

In this revision I have summarised all that has been published on the birds of The Gambia, much of it in roneoed papers which are not readily obtainable outside The Gambia or which are out of print, together with unpublished records up to January 1990.

A total of 507 species, in 74 families, has been reliably recorded; 18 species more than in 1979, including 2 which were placed in square brackets in the 1st Edition and 2 which were previously treated as sub-species. Eleven others, which the writer considers to be possible but unconfirmed, are included in square brackets. Two hundred and nineteen of the 507 species are known to have bred, 25 more than in 1979, but breeding data is still scanty and there are no fewer than 35 others which probably breed but which have never been proved to do so. It is also considered possible that a further 27 or so species might breed regularly or intermittently. Nineteen species which I have rejected are included also in square brackets and one species included in the 1st Edition has been deleted.

As can be readily seen, there are still many gaps in our knowledge. The true status of a number of species, particularly those which are confined to the few remaining areas of forest, is uncertain, and there are undoubtedly more casual visitors yet to be recorded. Since 1975, when The Gambia Ornithological Society began publishing bird reports (the first organised effort to record sightings) nearly 50 species have been added to the Gambian list, most of them vagrant Palaearctic migrants and African species which reach the northern limit of their range on the south bank of the Gambia River. Vagrant migrants, in particular, are likely to continue to swell the list as more bird-watchers, both local residents and experienced ornithologists who visit The Gambia on bird-watching holidays, look out for them. In addition, as the desert moves inexorably southwards, more sub-Saharan species will probably be reported on the north bank of the River.

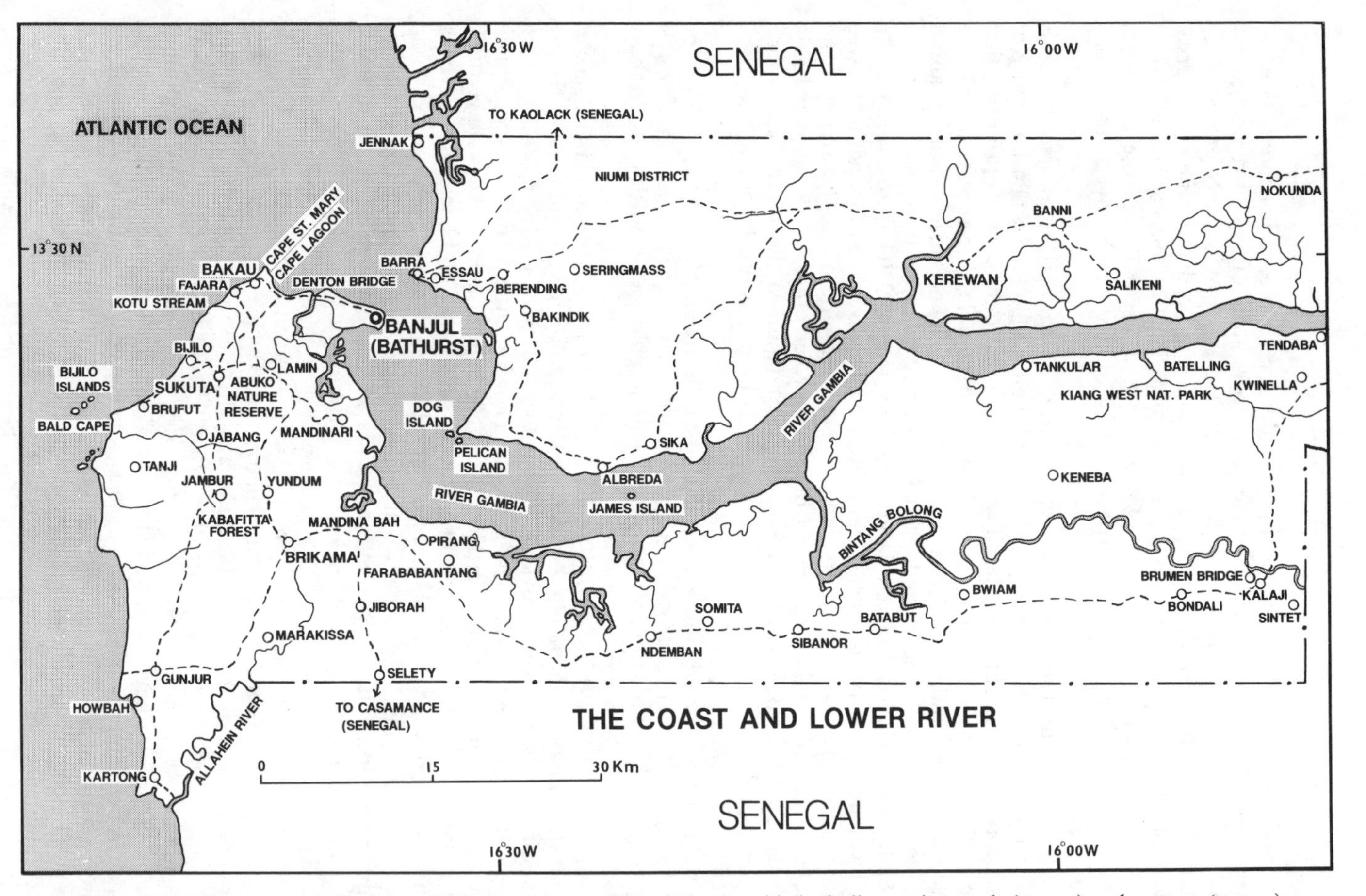

Figure 1. The main towns of the Coast and Lower River region of The Gambia including major roads (– – – –) and streams (≈).

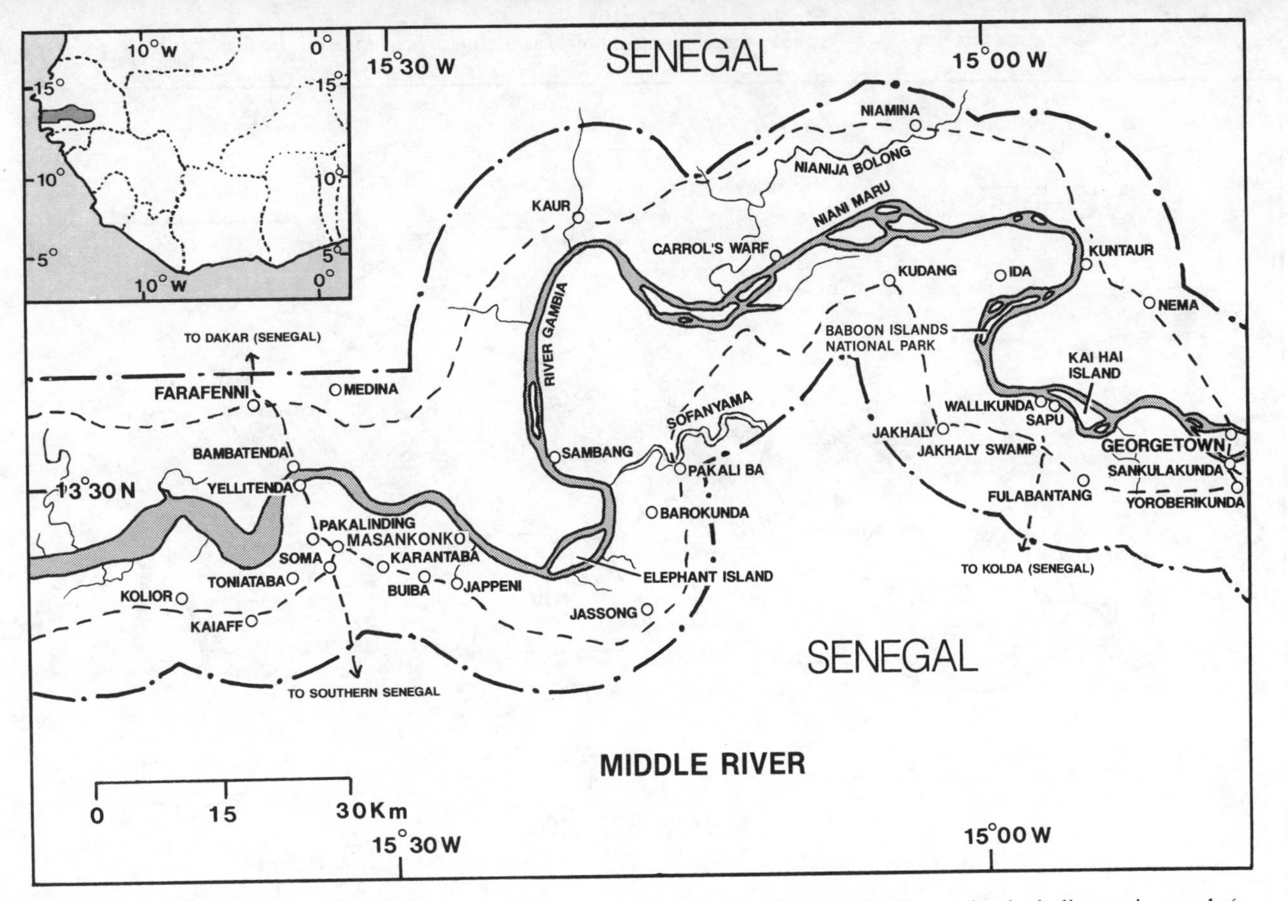

Figure 2. The position of The Gambia within West Africa and the main towns of the Middle River region including major roads (– – – –) and streams (〰).

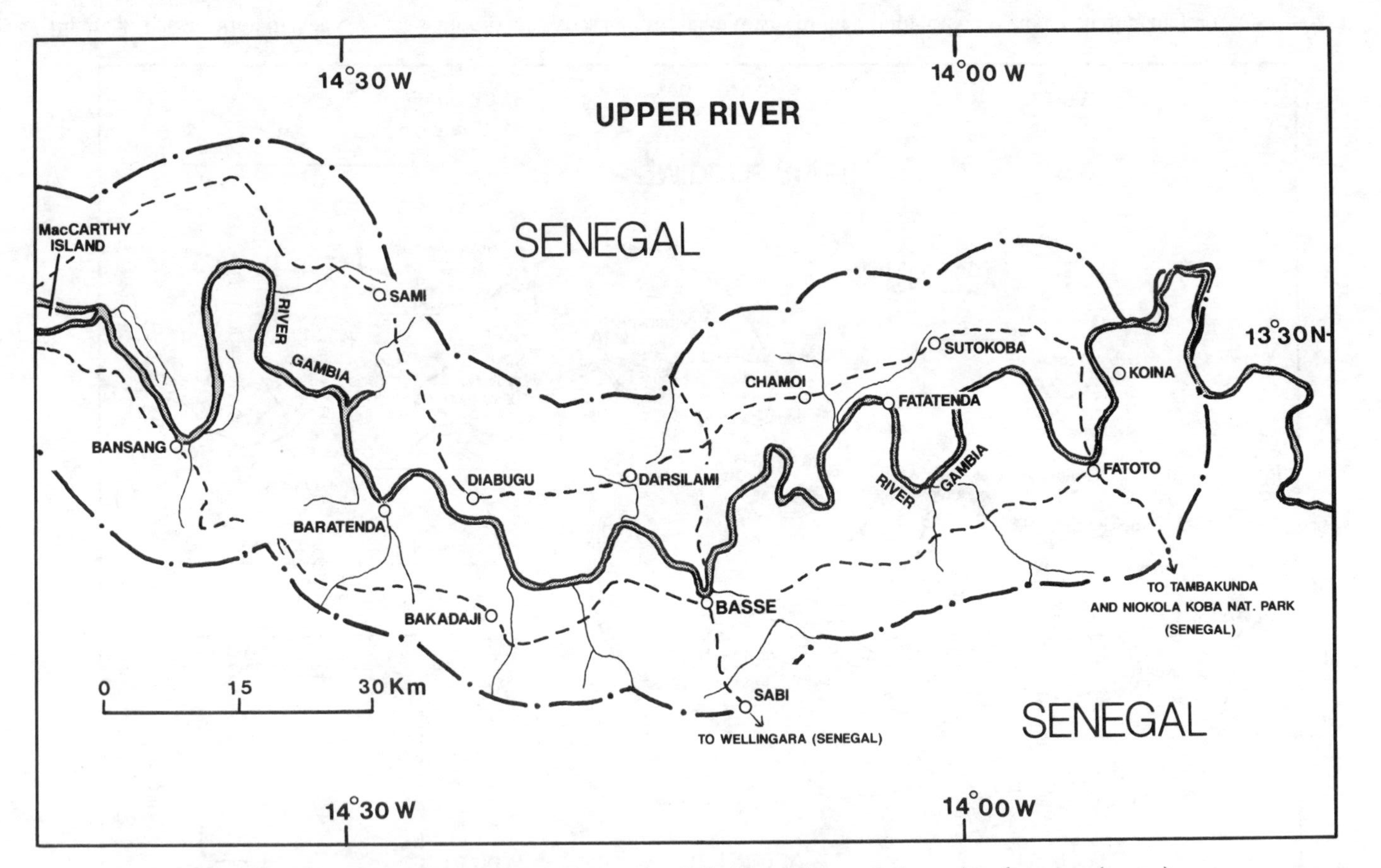

Figure 3. The main towns of the Upper River region including major roads (– – – –) and streams (≈≈).

A BRIEF HISTORY OF GAMBIAN ORNITHOLOGY

Several early travellers who visited West Africa in the eighteenth and nineteenth centuries took back to Europe collections they had obtained in 'Senegambia'. These travellers were mostly French, for The Gambia was a tiny British enclave in the middle of French West Africa. No definite locality was attached to these collections, but a number of specimens undoubtedly originated in The Gambia, for 'Senegambia' covered a vague area between the Senegal and Casamance rivers. However, only two species were named after The Gambia, the Spur-winged Goose *Plectropterus gambensis* and the Puff-back Shrike *Dryoscopus gambensis*, whereas no fewer than 17 birds bear the specific name *senegala, senegallus* or *senegalensis*.

The most important of these early naturalists was the botanist M. Adanson, who discovered both the Baobab Tree *Adansonia digita*, which Linnaeus named in his honour, and the Quail *Coturnix coturnix*. He spent several years in Senegal and visited The Gambia between 1748 and 1753. His '*Histoire Naturelle du Senegal*', published in Paris in 1757, contained observations on the birds he had encountered. No attempt was made to separate the species he collected in The Gambia from his Senegal collections.

The earliest collection known to have definitely come from The Gambia was obtained by Mr George Rendall, the first Lieutenant Governor, and was exhibited at the Zoological Society of London in 1835 (*Proc. Zool. Soc. Lond.:* 103). This collection formed the basis of 2 small volumes on the birds of West Africa by William Swainson which were published as part of the Naturalists Library in 1837.

The first important published work on the wildlife of the region was in French; Rochebrune's *Fauna de la Senegambia* (published about 1886) of which Volume 2 dealt with the birds. The following year a list of the birds of The Gambia by Captain G. E. Shelley appeared as an appendix to Alfred Moloney's *Forestry of West Africa* and listed 134 species.

The first paper in English dealing specifically with Gambian birds was 'Notes on the Ornithology of The Gambia' by Dr Percy Rendall in 1892 (*Ibis* Ser. 6 (4): 215–230). Dr Rendall spent 21 months in The Gambia in 1889–90 and covered mainly the birds of Bathurst (now Banjul) and its environs. This account was followed in 1901 by 'On the Ornithology of The Gambia River' by John Samuel Budgett (*Ibis* Ser. 8 (1): 481–496) which dealt with a collection of birds made during an expedition to study the fishes of the river in 1898–99.

From 1901 until 1929 Dr Emilius Hopkinson was Medical Officer and Travelling Commissioner for the Colonial Government. An aviculturalist, he published notes on the birds of The Gambia in the *Avicultural Magazine* in 1908 and 1909 and on the gamebirds and pigeons in the same publication in 1923. His *List of the Birds of The Gambia*, partly published in 1919, was never finished, only part of the passerines being completed. He also contributed a chapter on birds to Henry F. Reeve's *The Gambia* (1912: Smith Elder and Co.) and much of the information on The Gambia in Bannerman's 8-volume work *The Birds of Tropical West Africa* (1930–51) and the 2-volume abridged version *The Birds of West and Equatorial Africa* was derived from his previously unpublished records. In late 1928 and early 1929, shortly before he finally left The Gambia, Dr Hopkinson was joined by Willoughby Lowe and together they made a large collection for the British Museum (Natural History). No special report on this collection was published but Bannerman examined it and included all the new material in his two works.

From 1923 until 1963, little other than the occasional specific note was published on Gambian birds, though there were a number of people who took an interest in the subject. From 1939–52 Mr R. J. A. Walton, an oologist, made a private collection of eggs, part of which is now housed at State House, in Banjul, and which I have examined. In 1948 a group of biologists from Oxford and Cambridge visited The Gambia and one of them, Dr Norman Moore, an entomologist, made notes on the birds. Dr Ian McGregor joined the British Medical Research Council Laboratories at Fajara in 1949 and was Director from 1951–73 and again in 1978–79. He watched birds, mainly in the Fajara area and at Keneba, but also on his extensive travels throughout the country. Others who watched birds during this period and whose records have been incorporated here are I. Coghill (1959–66), Mr and Mrs V. E. Davies (1956–59), Mr and Mrs P. A. Gore (1959–65), K. G. S. Smith (1956–62) and K. M. Stevens (1946–49).

In 1960 E. M. Cawkell, an education officer who had lived in the country since 1956, produced a brief 'Notes from The Gambia', amending the range of 4 species (*Ibis* 102: 136–7) and in 1963 'Notes on the Birds of The Gambia', a joint paper with R. E. Moreau, who visited The Gambia and Senegal specifically to look at birds for 8 weeks in 1960–61 (*Ibis* 105: 156–178). In 1965 Cawkell produced further 'Notes on Gambian Birds' (*Ibis* 107: 535–40) up-dating the earlier papers. The notes in all 3 papers were selected mainly to supplement and modify the information given in Bannerman's standard work. Another notable ornithologist who visited the country on several occasions during this period was Sir A. Landsborough Thomson, then the Second Secretary of the Medical Research Council.

The Gambia Government in 1964 published *A List of One Hundred Commonest Birds* which had previously appeared in roneoed form, describing the birds which visitors to the capital were most likely to see. A roneoed annotated list 'Notes on the Birds of The Gambia' by Mrs Diana Bray, J. R. Mulholland & A. Vittery (Bray *et al.*), which included all their personal records, was produced in 1966, with an addendum in 1967. Mrs Bray worked mainly on resident African birds around Banjul 1964–67; J. R. Mulholland was with the Agricultural Department 1961–65, stationed at Yoroberikunda in MacCarthy Island Division and covered the up-river birds, both residents and migrants; and Alan Vittery, who was with the British High Commission, made a detailed study of waders and migrant passerines in the Banjul area during 1965 and 1966. Two other ornithologists were resident in The Gambia between 1966 and 1969 — O. Andrews and T. V. Simms, who studied the birds of the Banjul–Abuko–Yundum area and organised annual duck counts in Middle River. They produced a second (1969) addendum to the Bray *et al.* list.

In 1972 Dr Gérard J. Morel, a professional ornithologist who spent many years at Richard-Toll in northern Senegal and visited The Gambia on several occasions, produced his *Liste Commentée des Oiseaux du Sénégal et de la Gambie* for the *Office de la Recherche Scientifique et Technique Outre-mer*. He published a supplement in 1980. A bird atlas *Les Oiseaux de Senegambie (avec cartes de distribution)* which he has produced with his wife, Marie-Yvonne, also a professional ornithologist, is in final preparation and due to be published in 1990.

The Gambia Ornithological Society (GOS) was formed in 1974 and the following year published, in roneoed form, a revised and up-dated edition of the Bray *et al.* list edited by the late Miss Jean Garlick, which included recent observations by members and visitors, mainly from Britain and Scandinavia. From 1975–81 the Society produced an Annual Bird Report, the first 3 reports being edited by this author. No reports were published from 1982–85 but in 1986 the Society produced a Rarities Report covering the period 1982–86 and subsequently re-introduced an Annual Report in 1986–87.

Members of the Society who contributed the bulk of the records both for the revised (1975) edition of the Bray *et al.* list and the Annual Bird Reports 1975–79 were: Mrs M. Batty and Lady Bridges, both residents of Banjul; Dr R. S. Bray, Director of the Medical Research Council Laboratories 1973–77; C. V. Eyre, who was Education Officer with the Agricultural Department at Cape St Mary, 1972–82, and his sons Nicholas and Jonathan Eyre; Dr Angela Fuller, Medical Officer with The Gambia Government; Dr Richard Knight, who was at the Medical Research Council Laboratories 1975–76; Borge Palm, who stayed at Tendaba in 1973–74; R. H. Pickering, who was stationed at Yundum 1972–73 and then at Sapu Agricultural Station in Middle River, 1973–75; and Dr M. E. Smalley, who was at the Medical Research Council Laboratories 1974–82 and edited the Annual Bird Reports 1978–80. The present author was British Deputy High Commissioner in The Gambia from 1974 to 1978 and during this period travelled extensively throughout the country. He paid brief return visits to The Gambia in March and October 1989.

Other contributors to the earlier reports were: Dr Joan Bryan, Dr D. Clifford, P. Evans, D. Fisher, P. Goll, R. Hume, P. Manser, Amberley Moore, Dr Shiona Sowa and Chris White who, since 1978, has been Chairman of The Gambia Ornithological Society; visitors who contributed records were: Michael J. Allen, John S. Armitage, Kevin & Christine Carlson, J. N. Dymond, R. & J. Evans, G. des Forges, H. Gilston, J. de R. Kent, Guy Mountfort, C. W. G. Paulson-Ellis and M. Wright from Britain; Goran Blidberg, Bjorn Christophersen, Etienne Edberg, Knud Freisleben, J. V. Jensen, K. Kirkeby, Olvar Laessoe, Eigil Larson, Jan Michaelsen, Bent Pors Nielsen, Kaj Nielsen, Stig Kjaergaard Rasmussen, Annette & Uno Under and Anders Wirdheim from Scandinavia.

In 1980, without reference to The Gambia Ornithological Society, 2 Danish ornithologists, J. V. Jensen & K. Kirkeby, who had paid several visits to The Gambia in the 1970s, produced their *The Birds of The Gambia* published in Denmark. This contained the records of visiting bird-watchers, mostly from Scandinavia, and records extracted from GOS Annual Bird Reports. Many of the records were provided by well-known, competent ornithologists but others were of doubtful validity.

The 1981 GOS Annual Bird Report (published in 1983) was edited by J. M. Chapman, who was employed by the Public Works Department. Several of those who had contributed to the earlier reports also supplied records; other contributors were: Helen & Clive Lee, Richard Lorand, Marilyn Piddcock, Stefan Pihl, Stan da Prato, R. F. Porter, A. J. Smith and P. Walsh.

Contributors to the Rarities Report, 1982–86, and the 1986–87 Annual Bird Report (edited by Peter Byass, a scientist at the Medical Research Council Laboratories since 1984) were: P. Ames (who worked in The Gambia, 1981–84 and systematised the records for this period, which formed the basis of the Rarities Report), T. Andrews, D. Baldock, C. R. Barlow (who runs Sou-Manga Bird Tours in Fajara), P. C. Boon, C. Bradshaw, R. Bradshaw, E. Brewer (Director of Wildlife Conservation who established Abuko Nature Reserve in 1968), C. Cederlund, P. Chadwick, S. J. & R. N. Chadwick, J. Chapman, Dr Derek Clifford (who was at the Medical Research Council Laboratories at Fajara, 1974–80 and since 1984 has been at the International Trypanotolerence Centre; he is currently Recorder of the GOS), L. Cray, L. Davidson, T. Dean, A. J. & S. J. Duff, Dr Martin Eccles, D. Fisher, G. H. Gallimore, Dr B. M. Greenwood (Director of the Medical Research Council Laboratories since 1980), F. Groupe, A. Haines, D. Holman, A. Hunter, A. Ibbott (British High Commissioner since 1988), J. M. B. King, G. Langsbury, D. Moss, D. Orchard, J. Parrott, B. Pearson, M. Pedersen, M. J. Pointon, N. Powell, Graham Rainey (who since 1982 has run up-river cruises on the 'Spirit of Galicia'), D. Reynold, N. & E. Riddiford, L. A. Samuelson, A. & R. Scott, W. Serle, D. Taylor, T. Toohig, N. Tucker, A. & H. Tye, J. D. R. Vernon, B. Walls, T. Wacher, Prof W. E. Waters, R. Webzell, and J. Williams.

In addition, the following visiting groups submitted records: Messrs Archen, Bent, Clement and Davies, P. Donnelly and B. Macdonald (who carried out research at Kuntaur, Jan-Mar 1988), Farnham *et al.*, Hall, Henry & Gallimore, Horrocks, Kemefick, Lafranz *et al.*, B. Little *et al.* and Rawcliff *et al.*

I have also received personal communications, enclosing their observations made during visits to The Gambia, from R. J. Chandler (Jan 1988), J. N. Dymond (Nov–Dec 1986, Nov–Dec 1987 and Nov 1988) and B. Wright (Jul 1984).

In 1985–86 The Gambian–German Forestry Project (GGFP) sponsored a comprehensive ecological study of a forest island at Pirang, Lower River, which was published in 1988. Herman Ellenberg produced the section on birds in collaboration with Michael Mühlenberg. They observed 195 species in the 64 hectare study area including one new to The Gambia and several which are classed as being rare or little-known.

Finally, The Gambia Ornithological Society is endeavouring to ensure that all records of rare birds are properly substantiated. As can be seen in the systematic list, in the past a number of reported sightings have had to be discounted because the observers failed to provide sufficient information. The Society has produced, therefore, a Rare Bird Report Form which is reproduced on pp. 130–131. Ornithologists visiting The Gambia are asked to submit to the Society using this format their records of any new species, and all species described as 'vagrant' or 'rare' in this Check-list.

GEOGRAPHY, VEGETATION AND CLIMATE

The Republic of The Gambia lies on the west coast of Africa, between latitudes 13°03′N and 13°49′N and longitudes 16°46′W and 13°47′W. It forms an enclave in the Republic of Senegal and has a short seaboard on the Atlantic Ocean.

Geography

The Gambia is one of the smallest countries in Africa, with a total land area of only 10,367 km^2 and a population of a little over half a million. It lies within the valley of the Gambia River, the land stretching 322 km from east to west and varying in width from 48 km near the mouth of the river to about 24km further inland. The Gambia River is West Africa's finest waterway, rising in the Fouta Dialou plateau in Guinea (11°90′N, 11°38′W) and flowing through The Gambia for the last 475 km of its 1200 km course to the Atlantic. The river is tidal inland for about 200 km. At its mouth (Fig. 1) the river is 2·5 km wide; it then broadens to 13 km in the lower reaches, narrowing to 3 km wide 30 km upstream and is still 1 km wide at the trans-Gambia ferry crossing 132 km inland (Fig. 2). Thereafter it narrows to 800 m near Carrol's Wharf 209 km from the mouth, where the salinity ceases and upstream from there to the eastern end of the country it varies in width between 300 m and 600 m, with numerous islands in this section.

The country is flat, particularly near the sea, and nowhere does it rise more than 90 m above sea-level. The Atlantic coastline is mainly sandy beaches 20–50 m wide at low tide, backed by a low sandy cliff and broken by a few stretches of low laterite cliffs, the most prominent being at Fajara and Brufut (Fig. 1) where the laterite rises to a height of 8–12 m.

Dense mangrove swamps line the low, muddy river banks for the first 220 km upstream, with extensive mudflats exposed at low tide. Behind the mangrove are areas of savanna (see later) which are seasonally flooded. Near the coast much of this land is inundated with sea water and is therefore unsuitable for agriculture though dams are being constructed across many inlets to enable rice to be grown. Further up-river, where there is freshwater flooding during the rains, the land is under rice and an increasing area is being irrigated to produce two crops a year. Above Kuntaur (Fig. 2) the low-lying banks are bordered by dense riverine forest interspersed in places by red laterite outcrops up to 30 m high.

Away from the river, groundnuts, which contribute 90% of the country's exports, and to a lesser extent cereals for local consumption, are grown in the light sandy soils after the woodland and fallow bush has first been cleared. In the extreme eastern part of the country cotton has recently been introduced and it is expected that sugar, at present only planted on an experimental basis, will become an important crop on some of the many islands in the river.

The road network in The Gambia is among the best in Africa. A good road, much of it hard-topped, runs the length of the south bank with feeder roads down to the river every few miles. And on the north bank a dirt road runs inland from Barra to the Georgetown ferry, again with regular feeder roads to the river. There are also a number of feeder roads into Senegal on both banks.

In the 1st Edition I reported that there had been one major change in the geography of The Gambia in recent years: the virtual disappearance of the Bijilo Islands, once a string of sand islets off Bald Cape. In July 1948 Dr Norman Moore visited the islands and reported (Cawkell & Moreau — *Ibis* 105: 156–178) that a large area was well above high watermark and that the main islet, which covered an area of about 0·5 hectare, contained a grove of shrubs and trees, some of them 4–7 m high, in which he found nine nests of Sacred Ibis *Threskiornis aethiopica*, and saw about 500 Cattle Egrets *Ardeola ibis* and 500 West African Reef Egrets *Egretta gularis*, all of which may have been preparing to breed there. By 1961 all the trees had vanished, presumably the result of destruction by exceptionally high seas. In the 1970s the islands remained bare of vegetation except for a small area which contained some of the trailing creeper *Ipomoea* around the lighthouse and they appeared to be completely covered by water during spring tides. Since then the islands have built up again and today the main island stretches for several hundred metres even at the highest tides. In August 1989 C. R. Barlow saw *c.* 150 pairs of Caspian Terns *Sterna tschegrava* nesting amidst the *Ipomoea* creeper and it is likely that other species of birds breed on the islands at other times of the year.

Vegetation

The vegetation of much of The Gambia is savanna woodland with grass and shrub under-stories. The Gambia River is often loosely described as forming the dividing line between Guinea and Sudan savanna. In 1979 this was not strictly correct, for on the coast and through the western part of the country where it had not been disturbed, dense woodland similar to that found in the Guinea zone occurred on the north bank of the river. In contrast, in the central and eastern areas the vegetation on both banks was open savanna, typical of the Sudan zone. Today little, if any, Guinea savanna remains on the north bank and with the desert moving steadily southwards, desert scrub has replaced Sudan savanna to the river's edge along most of its length while deforestation on the south bank has reduced much of the remaining forest to open woodland. The river appears, however, still to form a barrier for several species of landbirds typical of the Guinea zone, which are at the extreme northern limit of their range in The Gambia and which have never been recorded on the north bank and several birds of desert scrub are confined to the north bank.

There are few areas which have not been modified by fire or by cultivation and which do not constitute secondary vegetation. The mangrove swamps are at present the least changed, though a considerable quantity of mangrove is cut for fuel;

and the proposed bridge-barrage across the river at the so-called Trans-Gambia ferry crossing at Farafenni, when completed, will result in the disappearance of all the mangrove above this point. In the estuary and along the creeks near the coast the mangrove is mostly the low *Avicennia africana*, but further upstream the river is bordered by the giant *Rhizophora racemosa*, which grows up to 25 m high; *R. harrisonii* and *R. mangle* occur at the boundary between *R. racemosa* and *A. africana* stands.

Except for the few forest parks and riverine forest, much of the country has been under repeated cultivation for at least 150 years. Its most impressive features are the tall, often spectacular, primary forest trees of economic importance, widely and sparsely scattered throughout cultivated areas, which have been spared. Typical of these are the Winter Thorn *Faidherbia (Acacia) albida*, Locust Bean *Parkia biglobosa*, Red Silk Cotton *Bombax costatum* and Mahogany *Khaya senegalensis*.

Fire is a major factor in controlling the vegetation; bush fires, often deliberately started by herdsmen, rage through the countryside during the dry season. Many tree species are specially adapted both by their growth rate and their bark to survive these fires, but few shrubs are able to do so, though they send up new shoots through the blackened soil within a few days of the passing of a fire. Around villages Mangoes *Mangifera indica*, Baobabs *Adansonia digita*, Kapoks *Ceiba pentandra* and Kolas *Cola cordifolia* predominate, many of them having been planted. Near the coast and in low-lying valleys inland, where there is a relatively high water table, there are extensive stands of Rhun Palms *Borassus aethiopium*.

Where woodland has remained relatively undisturbed, that in the western part of the country is noticeably taller and denser than in the east and is dominated by *Daniellia oliveri*, a species typical of the northern Guinea zone, which reaches the limit of its range in western Gambia. Typical larger trees in this zone are *Pterocarpus erinaceus, Terminalia albida, Parkia biglobosa, Khaya senegalensis, Bombax buonopozense* and *Ficus* spp, mainly *F. ingens* and *F. capensis*. Common smaller trees in *Daniellia* woodland are *Lannea velutina, Piliostigma thonningii, Prosopis africana, Acacia sieberiana* and *A. macrostachya*. The commonest large shrub is *Combretum micranthum*, which occasionally develops into a small tree form.

In the drier east of The Gambia *Daniellia oliveri* is absent and *Khaya senegalensis* is usually restricted to damper sites; the trees are generally smaller and the canopy thinner. Common larger trees are *Anogeissus leiocarpus Pterocarpus erinaceus, Bombax buonopozense* and *Sterculia setigera*.

Outside the forest parks most woodland has been much disturbed by the heavy human and cattle populations, and in cattle districts most trees are mutilated. Land standing fallow is rapidly covered with shrubs, particularly *Icacina senegalensis* and *Combretum glutinosum* and immature tree species, including the common and widespread *Terminalia albida, T. macroptera, Cordyla pinnata, Cassia sieberiana, Swartzia madagascariensis, Prosopis africana, Pterocarpus erinaceous* and *Acacia* spp. As a result of fire and grazing the herbaceous layer has been reduced to a small number of species. *Diheteropogon hagerupii, Pennisetum hordeoides, Loudetia simplex, Schizachyrium exile, Schoenefeldia gracilis, Ctenium elegans, Pennisetum pedicellatum, Andropogon* spp and *Hyparhenia* spp are most common.

The middle and eastern parts of the country have extensive grassy floodplains with grasses growing to heights of 65–165 cm during the rains. Grasses include *Anadelpha arrecta, Eragrostis atrovirens, Panicum anabaptistum, Vetivera nigritana* and, around the edges of swamps, *Schizachryrium brevifolium* and *Paspalum* spp. Although most of the floodplains are treeless, scattered low trees of *Mitragyne inermis* occur in some areas in Middle River. Behind the mangrove in Lower River are areas of taller grassland dominated by *Phragmites karha* and *Echinochloa pyramidalis*.

The Gambia River is the country's outstanding geographical feature. The Palm-nut Vulture *Gypohierax angolensis* (above) is resident along its length, while the West African River (or Fish) Eagle *Haliaetus vocifer* occurs mainly up-river.

A Long-tailed Shag *Phalacrocorax africanus* dries its wings in the sun. It is common along the length of the river and breeds colonially in Middle River.

Most of the coastline comprises sandy beaches. The Royal Tern *Sterna maxima* (above) is common and probably breeds, but no colonies are now known. A White-fronted Sand-Plover *Charadrius marginatus* pictured in 1976 near Tanji about to settle on eggs which are partly buried to protect them from the sun. In the 1970s several pairs were resident on sand-dunes along the coast. Since then they appear to have moved away and there are no recent breeding records on the mainland but young have been seen on the Bijilo Is.

Great White Egret *Egretta alba* escorted by a Long-tailed Shag pictured in the estuary along Banjul Bund.

The dark-grey Reef Heron *Egretta gularis* (above) was previously considered a subspecies of the all white Little Egret *Egretta egretta* (below), but today they are accepted as true species. Both are common on the coast and along the lower reaches of the river, but only the Little Egret is seen up-river.

Goliath Heron *Ardea goliath* (above) with a tilapia fish and Black Herons *Egretta ardesiaca* in their typical 'umbrella' fishing posture; 14 species of egrets and herons occur in the country.

Two specialist feeders, the African Spoonbill *Platalea alba* (above) and Yellow-billed Storks *Ibis ibis* are both found along the lower reaches of the river out of the breeding season. There are breeding colonies of the Storks in Middle River and the Spoonbill has recently been proved to breed, also in Middle River .

White Pelicans *Pelecanus onocrotalus* (above) and a Black-winged Stilt *Himantopus himantopus*; both are non-breeding visitors to The Gambia.

The Spur-winged Plover *Vanellus spinosus* (above) is common, always in the vicinity of water, while the Senegal Wattled Plover *Vanellus senegallus* occurs also in grassland and may often be seen on sports fields, particularly at Fajara.

More usually seen in swamplands this Spur-winged Goose *Plectropterus gambensis* (above) was perched high in a dead tree. White-faced Tree-ducks *Dendrocygna viduata* are the most abundant of the ducks and are found in wetlands throughout the country.

Thirty species of Palaearctic waders visit The Gambia either on passage or as winter visitors. Greenshank *Tringa nebularia* (above) are found singly on the edge of the mangrove swamps while Sanderling *Calidris alba* occur in flocks along the beaches.

Ruppell's Griffon Vulture *Gyps ruppellii* (above) and White-headed Vulture *Trigonoceps occipitalis*; both are scarce residents and are found mainly inland.

The Hooded Vulture *Neophron monachus* (above) is the common vulture of towns and villages throughout the country. Below: an African Hawk-eagle *Hieraaetus spilogaster,* a bird of open forest, pictured at its eyrie in Kabafitta forest, 20 metres up in a *Daniella oliveri*, a tree typical of the Guinea savanna zone.

The monotonous call of the Lemon-rumped Tinker-bird *Pogoniulus bilineatus* (above) is a familiar sound in gardens and open woodland. The Brown Babbler *Turdoides plebejus* occurs in similar habitat in noisy flocks; one is pictured here feeding a chick (probably a Levaillant's Cuckoo *Clamator levaillantii*) in a Fajara garden.

The Scops Owl *Otus scops* is resident and probably not uncommon in open woodland, but because of its cryptic colouration is rarely reported.

Two races of the Hoopoe *Upupa epops* occur in The Gambia. The local race *U. e. senegalensis* is a scarce breeding resident while the nominate European race is a winter visitor.

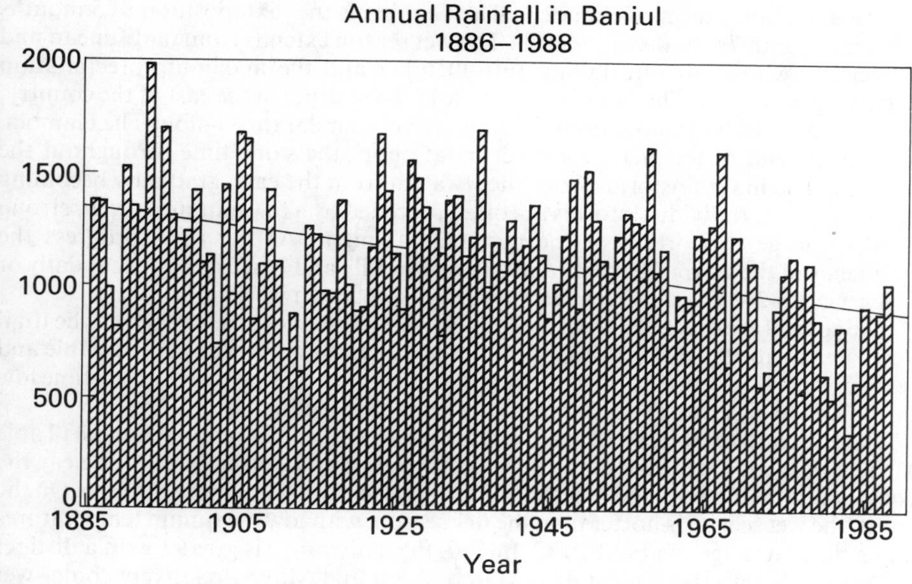

Figure 4. Annual Rainfall in Banjul, 1886–1988.

Table 1. Mean monthly maximum and minimum temperatures °C

	Jan	Feb	Mar	Apr	May	Jun	Jul	Aug	Sep	Oct	Nov	Dec
CAPE ST MARY												
maximum	28·3	27·7	27·6	27·4	27·6	30·1	29·8	29·3	30·0	30·6	30·4	28·8
minimum	18·2	18·4	18·9	19·8	21·0	23·4	23·5	23·2	23·3	23·3	22·2	19·4
BASSE												
maximum	34·9	37·6	39·8	40·9	40·7	36·4	32·8	31·6	32·4	33·6	35·0	33·8
minimum	14·5	17·0	18·6	21·8	24·0	23·4	22·8	22·1	22·1	22·7	20·0	15·6

On the barren flats, particularly in North Bank Division and Kiang West in Lower River (Fig. 1), where the soil is saline or acid, the succulent *Sesuvium portulacastrum* is characteristic, with the grasses *Paspalum vaginatum* and *Diplachne fusca* occurring in more favourable conditions.

The coastal sand-dunes have a sparse cover of *Aristida* spp, *Cenchrus biflora, Perutis patens* and *Aragrostis* spp with stunted Baobabs *Adansonia digitata*. Inland from the dunes there is a belt of low woodland dominated by *Parinari macrophylla*, with an understorey of tall grasses including *Heteropogon melanocarpa, Loudetia kagerensis* and *L. simplex*.

Climate

Climatic zones in West Africa are very narrow; a journey 100 km north or south will produce a greater change in vegetation pattern than one of 1000 km eastwards. Tropical rainforest becomes evident about 200 km south of The Gambia and desert is reached within 300 km north. The climate is, therefore, closer to that of Northern Nigeria, 2500 km to the east, than to that experienced 250 km north or south of The Gambia.

The dominant aspect of climate in The Gambia is the juxtaposition of 5 months wet season with 7 months dry season. The wet season extends from mid June to mid November with most rain falling July–October and the maximum precipitation occurring in August. The rains begin about 15 days earlier in the east of the country, but October and November rainfall totals are very similar throughout The Gambia, so that the end of the wet season occurs at about the same time throughout the country. The first rainstorms work their way in from the east, gradually becoming more frequent. Individual storms are often preceded by a few minutes of very strong wind. A large proportion of the rain falls at night. As the rains progress the frequency of the storms decrease and whereas in July and August they occur daily or at least every 2–3 days, by October they may be spaced a week apart.

The coastal area receives an average of about 1100 mm of rain a year, but the total decreases to about 1000 mm inland. Recently the rains have been very variable and semi-drought conditions occurred in 1977 and in the early 1980s with an all-time low in 1983. However, rainfall has increased since 1985 (see Fig. 4).

There is considerable variation in temperature regime through the Gambia (Table 1). The Atlantic Ocean moderates the temperature and diurnal variation near the coast, while inland both the diurnal and seasonal variation are more extreme. On the coast, the wet season is hotter than the dry season, with low maximum temperatures and a diurnal range of about 10°C. Inland, the daily range is greater with a distinct hot period before the rains in late March, April and May, a relatively cooler wet season and cold nights during the dry season. Humidity during the wet season is high, particularly in September and October when it can reach 95% on the coast.

HABITATS AND BIRD DISTRIBUTION

There are 10 types of habitat which can readily be distinguished in The Gambia, each of which is characterised by a number of common bird species either residents or migrant visitors. Clearly there is some overlap: a number of species which occur offshore, for example, are also found inland along the river, and some of the riverine forest birds occur also in open bush country and the larger suburban gardens. On the other hand, many species are strictly limited in their habitat requirements and are confined to one type only.

Offshore

Few true sea-birds occur in The Gambia. No auks or shearwaters have been recorded, but immature Gannets *Sula bassana* are regularly reported offshore and Storm and Wilson's Petrels *Hydrobates pelagicus* and *Oceanites oceanicus* occur in the estuary off Banjul. Storm Petrels are winter visitors from the north, though a few non-breeding birds have been reported over-summering; and Wilson's Petrel is an occasional visitor during the southern winter from its Antarctic breeding grounds.

Large numbers of terns pass through Gambian waters on migration or winter along the coast though some species which might be expected to occur are rarely seen; they presumably pass The Gambia at sea out of sight of land. Sandwich Terns *Sterna sandvicensis*, Royal Terns *Sterna maxima* and Caspian Terns *Sterna tschegrava* are numerous during the non-breeding season. Royal and Caspian Terns both nest in Senegal, the latter also in The Gambia, and some are present throughout the year. The Gambia has also recently been proved to be a formerly undiscovered wintering ground for Lesser Crested Terns *Sterna bengalensis*, presumably birds from the Mediterranean breeding colonies. A distinctive sight off Cape St Mary, Fajara and Denton Bridge during the migration periods are the tightly packed flocks of feeding Black Terns *Sterna nigra*. A few non-breeders remain and usually a small over-summering flock is present at Denton Bridge. Terns also occur commonly inland along the lower reaches of the river. Several hundred Lesser Black-backed Gulls *Larus fuscus* winter on the coast and occasionally Pomatorhine and Arctic Skuas, *Stercorarius pomarinus* and *S. parasiticus*, are reported.

Coastal beaches

The characteristic birds of the sandy beaches which, except for one or 2 laterite outcrops, stretch the length of the coast, are the flocks of Sanderling *Calidris alba* which are present from July until May. They occur both as passage migrants and winter visitors, the majority passing through August–October and March–April. The over-wintering flocks, usually numbering 15–30, arrive later and depart earlier. Each flock appears to occupy about half a mile of beach and there is recent evidence that the wintering flocks remain on the same stretch of beach throughout their stay. Grey Plovers *Pluvialis squatarola*, Oyster-catchers *Haematopus ostralegus* and Whimbrel *Numenius phaeopus* are also seen commonly along the beaches on migration and in winter.

In the 1970s several pairs of White-fronted Sand Plovers *Charadrius marginatus* were resident, nesting just above the high water mark at Cape St Mary and Tanji, but there are no recent breeding records. They have, however, been seen with young on the recently re-emerged Bijilo Is. and it may be that they have moved here from the mainland. Where the creeper *Ipomoea* has gained a foothold Crested Larks *Galerida cristata* occur. The latter are also found on open ground a few hundred yards in from the beach, but, rather surprisingly, are not found inland of the coastal strip. Terns and gulls roost on the beaches and Palm-nut Vultures *Gypohierax angolensis* scavenge along the tide-wrack as well as inland along the river. Pied Kingfishers *Ceryle rudis* excavate their nestholes in the laterite cliffs at Fajara, but also nest along the banks of the river.

Mudflats

The estuary of the Gambia river from Banjul inland for 100 km is an important resting and wintering ground for Palaearctic waders. At low tide the extensive mudflats provide feeding areas for as many as 20 species of waders. Large flocks of Curlew Sandpipers *Calidris ferruginea* and Little Stints *Calidris minuta* occur, while Redshank *Tringa totanus*, Greenshank *Tringa nebularia*, Marsh Sandpipers *Tringa stagnatalis*, Turnstone *Arenaria interpres*, Knot *Calidris canutus*, Dunlin *Calidris alpina*, Curlew *Numenius arquata* and Bar-tailed Godwits *Limosa lapponica* are all common either on the open mud or along the creeks which meander through the extensive areas of the small *Avicennia* mangrove. Largest numbers of waders occur on passage October–November and February–March, but many over-winter as well.

In the shallows, Pink-backed Pelicans *Pelecanus rufescens*, Yellow-billed Storks *Ibis ibis* and 5 species of herons and egrets are conspicuous. Grey-headed Gulls *Larus cirrhocephalus* are present throughout the year and White-winged Black Terns *Sterna leucoptera* are noticeable on their northern migration in April; they apparently by-pass The Gambia in the autumn, presumably passing further inland to their wintering ground further south.

The river

The Gambia River, one of the great waterways of Africa, is the country's outstanding geographical feature, and it is because of the river, and the swamps which border it during and after the rains, that The Gambia has such a rich avian fauna. The surrounding area is largely arid bush for 8 months of the year and many species which disperse away from the river during the rains to breed concentrate in the river's vicinity during the dry season. Six species of kingfisher occur along its banks, the Blue-breasted *Halcyon malimbica* and the Pied being most conspicuous. Three bee-eaters, the Blue-cheeked *Merops superciliosus*, Carmine *M. nubicus* and Red-throated *M. pusillus* are to be seen here, as well as in open country, while the Blue Fairy Flycatcher *Trochocercus longicauda* and Swamp Flycatcher *Muscicapa aquatica* are found only along the banks of Middle (Fig. 2) and Upper River (Fig. 3).

Flocks of Sand Martins *Riparia riparia* winter here and several species of swifts are noticeable feeding over the water. From December to March several thousand Garganey *Anas querquedula* are present on the section between Karantaba and Kaur (Fig. 2). The rafts of Garganey are often mixed with smaller flocks of Knob-billed Geese *Sarkidiornis melanota* and White-faced Tree Ducks *Dendrocygna viduata*, both African birds which do not migrate outside West Africa, and occasionally small parties of rare Palaearctic ducks are found in the mixed flocks. Most noticeable among the birds of prey on the river is the West African River or Fish Eagle *Haliaetus Vocifer*, whose ringing call can be heard the length of the river. Giant or Pel's Fishing Owls *Scotopelia peli* have been recorded only in Middle River, particularly on Baboon Is, but they probably also occur further upstream. Among the smaller birds Black-headed Weavers *Ploceus melanocephalus* are particularly abundant and their colonies line the banks for miles in Middle River. A little-seen bird which is widely distributed from the mangrove creeks near the coast inland along the river to the eastern end of the country is the Finfoot *Podica senegalensis*. Particularly secretive it spends most of the time swimming beneath tangled vegetation close to the bank, only occasionally venturing out into the open water.

Mangrove

Two types of mangrove occur in The Gambia. Near the coast on the river and along the small creeks which run into the sea, the small *Avicennia* mangrove covers the banks and in some places also large areas of mud, forming extensive thickets up to 5 m high. Further upstream the river is bordered by the giant *Rhizophora* which grows to 12 m high. Several species of herons and egrets nest in the mangrove and the Brown-necked Parrot *Poicephalus robustus* almost exclusively utilises holes high in the trunks of the *Rhizophora* for breeding. Mangrove is not, however, an important breeding habitat, though a few species which breed in low bushes on dry land sometimes make use of it. As neither *Avicennia* nor *Rhizophora* bears an edible fruit, the food available in mangroves for birds is limited to insects and they are now recognised mainly as an important habitat for wintering Palaearctic migrants. Of these the warblers, particularly the Subalpine Warbler *Sylvia cantillans*, Willow Warbler *Phylloscopus trochilus* and Chiffchaff *P. collybita* are the most evident.

Freshwater swamps and rice-fields

During the rains, which fall between June and October, most low-lying land is flooded. The ground quickly dries after the rains and then many of the birds which have dispersed away from the floods and river into Senegal return to congregate in the vicinity of the freshwater pools and marshes bordering the river, their concentration by the river increasing as the dry season progresses and the marshes dry up.

Sadly the most important freshwater swamp at Jakhaly, 270 km inland, where huge numbers of waterfowl and wading birds formerly concentrated from November until June has been drained. There in the 1970s the most spectacular sight was the flock of Crowned Cranes *Balearica pavonina* which was present annually. As the wet season approached the cranes paired up, though remaining within the flock, and then perhaps 50 could be seen together going through their strange, almost mystical, dancing display. Large flocks of Spur-winged Geese *Plectropterus gambensis* and Knob-billed Geese were also present at Jakhaly during this season. Today the large flocks have gone but Jacanas *Actophilornis africana* and Painted Snipe *Rostratula benghalensis* still occur in the ricefields and adjoining pools and Pigmy Geese *Nettapus auritus* are also present along with Purple and Allen's Gallinules *Porphyrio porphyrio* and *P. alleni*.

Jakhaly is now under rice cultivation, as indeed are most of the larger freshwater swamps, but there are many small marshes which are important refuges for water birds. Of these the best known is Camaloo, 40 hectares, beside the main road between Banjul and the residential area at Fajara on the Atlantic coast. No fewer than 176 species have been recorded from this small marsh and the surrounding scrub, including 14 species of herons and egrets, 10 of which can normally be seen on any day between December and May. Yellow-billed Storks, Hammerkops *Scopus umbretta* and Sacred Ibis *Threskiornis aethiopica* are all regular visitors, while African Spoonbills *Platalea alba* sometimes occur. Another swamp which holds large numbers of waders and waterbirds during the migration periods and lesser, but still substantial, numbers throughout the winter is behind Banjul Bund.

During the rains, when most birds breed, Yellow-crowned Bishops *Euplectes afer* and Yellow-mantled Widow-birds *Euplectes macrourus* are particularly noticeable in the vicinity of swamps and growing rice, while Yellow-throated Longclaws *Macronyx croceus* are found in the open ground bordering the wetlands. Many Palaearctic waders, particularly Wood Sandpipers *Tringa glareola* and Green Sandpipers *Tringa ochropus* occur as passage migrants and winter visitors in the drainage channels between the ricefields, and flocks of Black-tailed Godwits *Limosa limosa* feed on the growing rice.

Riverine and canopy forest

Formerly much of the south bank of the river inland as far as Bwiam (Fig. 1) was densely forested with high Guinea savanna, but today most of this forest has been cleared and only small pockets survive, mainly in the triangle formed by Abuko, Brufut and Brikama. Dense riverine forest occurs along the south bank above Kaur and on the numerous islands in Middle River (Fig. 2). Typical of the high Guinea savanna are several bird species which reach the northern limit of their range in The Gambia. Of these the most noticeable is the Allied Hornbill *Tockus fasciatus* which is quite common in the Abuko–Brufut–Brikama triangle (Fig. 1), but is not found elsewhere.

Abuko Nature Reserve remains the best example of canopy forest and several species have been recorded only from there; doubtless they also occur in other tracts of similar forest, though these are fast disappearing, and it is very probable that they have been overlooked. White-breasted Cuckoo-Shrikes *Coracina pectoralis* are resident but local in the remaining high forest in Lower River, while Red-shouldered Cuckoo-Shrikes *Campephaga phoenicea* also occur in riverine forest inland. Other typical birds of this habitat are Mohos *Hypergerus atriceps*, Blue-bills *Spermophaga haematina* and several species of sunbird.

Open woodland and secondary bush; gardens

Inland where the land is not under cultivation, most of the country is covered with open Sudan savanna woodland, secondary scrub and bush; the larger gardens, particularly on the coast of Fajara, offer a similar type of habitat. More than 160 species occur here of which the seed-eaters and starlings are probably the most noticeable; fruit is also abundant and provides an important source of food. Eight weavers are found exclusively in this open woodlands, the flocks making forays into the maize and ricefields to feed. Sunbirds, too, are common while 7 species of shrike, of which the striking Gonolek or Barbary Shrike *Laniarius barbarus* is the most obvious, 4 woodpeckers and 7 flycatchers, including the beautiful Red-bellied Paradise Flycatcher *Terpsiphone rufiventer*, occur.

Numbers of Palaearctic migrants utilise this habitat either on passage or as winter visitors. Both Pied and Spotted Flycatchers *Ficedula hypoleuca* and *Muscicapa striata* are common on passage, particularly in late September and October, while Redstarts *Phoenicurus phoenicurus* and Nightingales *Luscinia megarhynchos* occur throughout the winter.

Cleared agricultural land, grassland

Much of the country has been under repeated cultivation for nearly two centuries, but the clearing of woodland has intensified over the past 30 years. However, many tall, often spectacular trees have been spared and these constitute the most impressive feature of the countryside. Many species which nest and roost in woodland, including nearly all the small seed-eating birds, feed in these open fields. Seven species of resident doves are widespread and common and in Middle River (Fig. 2). Their numbers are augmented in some years by millions of Turtle Doves *Streptopelia turtur* for a few weeks in late February and March, a concentration which probably comprises a fair proportion of the western European breeding population. The time spent by Turtle Doves in The Gambia is presumably used to build up fat reserves for the return journey across the Sahara to Europe to breed.

Two very different birds are characteristic of the open fields. The Abyssinian Ground Hornbill *Bucorvus abyssinicus* and the Standard-wing Nightjar *Macrodipteryx longipennis* are widely distributed, though nowhere common; the former, turkey-sized and ungainly, the latter known in Mandinka as 'the bird with four wings' from the elongated shafts which the male bird sprouts during the breeding season. One species of sand-grouse, the Four-banded Sand-grouse *Pterocles quadricinctus* is particularly common in Middle (Fig. 2) and Upper River (Fig. 3) and at dusk large numbers can be seen flying to their watering places along the river; a few pairs nest in Lower River, particularly on the open ground immediately behind the sand-dunes on the coast. The Gambia's only common game bird, the Double-spurred Francolin *Francolinus bicalcaratus* feeds in the open fields in the early morning and late evening but roosts and spends the heat of the day amidst the trees. Flocks of Quail Finches *Ortygospiza atricollis* are encountered in open grassland, usually, but not invariably, in the vicinity of water.

Two of the large plovers which are resident in The Gambia, the Wattled Plover *Vanellus senegallus* and Black-headed Plover *Vanellus tectus*, are found on dry open ground; the third, the Spur-winged Plover *Vanellus spinosus*, is always associated with water.

The tall trees which have survived the agriculturalists and annual fires which rage across much of the country during the early months of the year provide nesting sites for 3 species of vulture, Buffalo Weavers *Bubalornis albirostris*, and, in Middle and Upper River only, for about 200 pairs of Marabou Storks *Leptoptilus crumeniferus*, colonies of 5–20 pairs being found along the roadside between Jappeni and Georgetown.

Towns and villages

The characteristic bird associated with human habitation is the Hooded Vulture *Neophron monachus*, which occurs in towns and villages throughout the country and often breeds in tall trees amidst houses. The Black-headed Village Weaver *Ploceus cucullatus* also favours trees in villages in which to nest colonially. Surprisingly, though these latter consume vast quantities of grain, the nests are rarely destroyed by the villagers. The beautiful little Senegal or Red-billed Fire-Finch *Lagonosticta senegala* and Red-cheeked Cordon-bleu *Estrilda bengala* are also common around villages, though both are also widely distributed in the open countryside as well. *L. senegala*, which will nest practically anywhere, is often parasitised by the Green Indigo-bird *Vidua chalybeata*. *E. bengala* nests usually near wasps' nests. In 1981 the House Sparrow *Passer domesticus* arrived at Banjul, probably on board a vessel from Dakar where the species established itself in the 1970s. It is now well-established in the city and its environs but to-date has not extended its range further inland.

BREEDING

Breeding data is particularly sparse and, as can be seen from the Systematic List, there are no fewer than 35 species which appear to be resident and therefore must nest in The Gambia but have not yet been proved to do so. Because of the dearth of data, only approximate breeding dates can be given for many species; but recent studies by members of The Gambia Ornithological Society have shown that for some birds the breeding season is more extended than was previously believed to be the case. The 'breeding season' in The Gambia is generally considered to be during the rains, late June–early November, and for most species this is approximately correct; but several species have an extended season covering 8–9 months and breed in both the wet and dry seasons, while some nest mainly in the dry season and a very few may be found nesting throughout the year.

All passerines which feed their young on regurgitated seeds or a mixed diet of seeds and insects breed during the latter part of the rains, between August and December, when the grasses and grain crops are ripening. This group includes most of the Ploceidae, of which the weavers and bishops are most evident, for the males are seasonally dimorphic and assume a brilliant nuptial plumage of yellow and black or red and black, and also the Fringillidae, Emberizidae and the Estrildidae. Nesting in some species of estrildids extends into the dry season and *Lagonosticta senegala* appears to breed throughout the year.

Nearly all passerines which feed their young exclusively on a diet of insects, start building and laying in late May or ealy June so that hatching coincides with the start of the rains in late June when insect prey becomes abundant almost overnight. Predation is high and many make several attempts before successfully raising a brood. Some species may in fact be double or even treble brooded, but there is no evidence of this. Breeding extends through November and occasionally into December. This group includes the Campephagidae, Pycnonotidae, Laniidae, Muscicapidae, Oriolidae and Dicruridae. The only non-passerines which are strictly limited to this season are the Cuculidae, most of which are parasitic on such passerines.

The breeding season for some non-passerines e.g. water birds and those which feed their young mainly on a diet of insects, is closely linked to the rains, though the water birds, in particular, continue breeding for 2–3 months into the dry season, when the freshwater marshes are still flooded. Of the other non-passerines, fruit-eaters generally start nesting during the rains so that the young hatch at the start of the dry season when most trees begin to fruit. The Accipitridae, Falconidae and most ground-nesting species breed exclusively during the dry season, starting shortly after the rains have ended and continuing through until April or even May.

The following analysis, by family, is based only on definite evidence of breeding (nest-building, eggs or young in the nest, young recently out of the nest, etc.). Those families for which breeding has never been proved are not considered. Numerals in brackets refer to the species in the Systematic List. It is perhaps helpful to restate that the rains begin in the second half of June and end in early November.

Pelecanidae (5–6), **Phalacrocoracidae** (9–10), **Anhingidae** (11), **Ardeidae** (13–29), **Ciconiidae** (31–37), **Threskiornithidae** (38–42) and **Gruidae** (118). The larger species breed during the latter part of the rains, September–October and continue into the dry season, with young fledging February–March. The smaller species generally nest earlier, starting in June or July, their young mostly fledging October–November, though fledged young have been seen in September and December.

Scopidae (30). Nest-building noted in June, so that breeding is probably confined to the rains, June–November.

Anatidae (45–58) and **Jacanidae** (132). Mainly confined to the rains, most young hatch September–November, but recently fledged *Actophilornis africana* have been seen March and June.

Accipitridae (60–100), **Falconidae** (102–110), **Tytonidae** (246) and **Strigidae** (247–253). Breeding is mainly confined to the early part of the dry season, with most young hatching February–March and fledging April–May. Some species start nesting towards the end of the rains, October–November, and *Haliaetus vocifer* has been found with newly fledged young in the nest in November.

Phasianidae (111–116). Breeding occurs in both wet and dry seasons; most probably start nesting towards the end of the rains, September–October, and continue until April. Young of *Ptilopachus petrosus* have been recorded in July.

Turnicidae (117) and **Pteroclididae** (214–215). Breeding is confined to the middle of the dry season, January–April; most chicks hatch in March.

Rallidae (119–126) and **Heliornithidae** (127). Mainly breed in the rains but chicks have been seen in January. *Limnocorax flavirostra* may breed at any time when swamp conditions are suitable.

Otididae (128–131). The only breeding records are of *Eupodotis melanogaster* in August and *E. senegalensis* in February, so that breeding probably extends throughout the dry season and into the rains.

Rostratulidae (133). Once collected and described as 'laying' in December. There is no other evidence to indicate the breeding season, and dates are unknown also in Senegal.

Burhinidae (137–138) and **Charadriidae** (144–158). Mainly dry season nesters, breeding sometimes extending into the rains. *Burhinus senegalensis* has been found with eggs April–May and October, *Vanellus spinosus* breeding December–July and *V. senegallus* October–July. All records for *Charadrius marginatus* show chicks May-June.

Glareolidae (139–143). *Cursorius temminckii* breeds at the start of the dry season, with chicks February–March. *Glareola pratincola* has been suspected of breeding in June.

Laridae (187–212). Mainly wet season breeders, probably starting just before the rains begin. *Larus cirrocephalus* was observed copulating in May and July and *Sterna albifrons* seen with chicks in August.

Columbidae (216–227). Most start nesting towards the end of the rains, October–November, and continue into the dry season until March–April. *Columba guinea* probably breeds throughout the year.

Musophagidae (231–233) and **Psittacidae** (228–230). Breeding is mainly confined to the dry season, December–May; but *Crinifer piscator* was found once with eggs in October and *Poicephalus senegalus* with flying young in September and at a nesthole in October.

Cuculidae (234–245), **Pycnonotidae** (339–345), **Laniidae** (346–356), **Muscicapidae** (357–424), **Oriolidae** (501–502), and **Dicruridae** (503–504). Breeding extends from the latter part of the dry season through the rains until November, occasionally December. **Campephagidae** (337–338) has been recorded breeding only at the end of the dry season and the early part of the rains, June–August.

Caprimulgidae (254–258). Dry season breeders, sometimes extending into the early part of the rains, December–July.

Apodidae (259–264). *Apus affinis* colonies are occupied twice during the year, January–February and July–August. *Cypsiurus parvus* has an extended season, but mostly nests during the rains, June–October.

Alcedinidae (266–274). Most nest just before and during the rains, May–October but *Ceryle rudis* has been recorded August–October and December–February, *C. maxima* November–February and *Halcyon leucocephalas* only in the dry season, April–June.

Meropidae (275–282) and **Coraciidae** (283–287). Most appear to breed towards the end of the dry season and into the rains, April–July, but *Merops bulocki* and *M. nubicus* have been reported as entering cliff nesting holes in Upper River January–April; this would conform with their nesting season in Senegal.

Upupidae (288). *Upupa epops* has been recorded nesting March–April and *Phoeniculus purpureus* [**Phoeniculidae** (289–290)] has an extended season throughout the rains, June–November.

Bucerotidae (291–294). All start breeding in the rains and are feeding young during the first 3 months of the dry season, November–January, when most trees are fruiting; *Bucorvus abyssinicus* was feeding young in October.

Capitonidae (295–298). Breeds mainly during the rains, but starts at the end of the dry season and sometimes continues into December. **Indicatoridae** (299–301) are normally parasitic on Capitonidae, but *Indicator indicator* being fed by *Merops pusillus* in July is the only record.

Picidae (302–309). Breeding recorded throughout the year. Most appear to nest at the end of the dry season with young being fed February–August. *Mesopicos goertae* is confined to the dry season, with young in April.

Alaudidae (310–314) and **Motacillidae** (329–336). Ground nesters breeding during the dry season. *Macronyx croceus* extends its breeding into the rains, June–July.

Hirundinidae (315–328). Breeds mainly during the dry season, February–May, but *Hirundo senegalensis* breeds during the rains and *H. smithii* has been recorded breeding August–May, with apparent peaks February–March and August–September.

Remizidae (425), **Paridae** (426) and **Zosteropidae** (438). All breeding records are for the dry season, January–May.

Nectariniidae (428–437). Breeding is recorded throughout the year, *Nectarinia coccinigaster* and *N. cuprea* just before and during the rains, April–October, the others during the dry season, sometimes continuing into the rains, December–July.

Emberizidae (439–442) and **Ploceidae** (464–490). Breed during the rains, August–November, though a few may start before the rains, sometimes as early as April.

Fringillidae (443–444), which feed their young on regurgitated seeds, breed towards the end of the rains and into the dry season, October–December.

Estrildidae (445–463), though most breeding is concentrated during the rains, August–November, have an extended season and *Logonosticta senegala* appears to breed throughout the year.

Sturnidae (491–500) and **Corvidae** (505–507). Breeding is confined to the end of the dry season and the early part of the rains, April–June

MIGRATION AND MOVEMENTS

Four types of migrant can be recognised in The Gambia. Most numerous are the Palaearctic migrants, of which 62 are mainly passage visitors with only a few individuals or small flocks over-wintering; 9 are purely passage migrants, going much further south across the African continent to spend the winter; 26 can be considered mainly as winter visitors; and there are another 42 irregular or accidental visitors and vagrants. A great deal of research has been carried out on Palaearctic migrants in Africa, and in The Gambia there is considerable data on one group, the waders (see below), but less is known about passerine and other visitors. The Gambia does not appear to be an important wintering ground for many species and most Palaearctic birds can be considered as passage migrants with a few individuals remaining through the winter.

Two forms of intra-African migration are evident: non-breeding visitors and migrant breeders. 23 species occur as non-breeding visitors, being present during the dry season from November until May; a further 50 species can be classified as accidental visitors or vagrants under this heading. In addition 3–4 non-breeding visitors occur during the rains.

There are 7 migrant breeders which are present in The Gambia only during and immediately after the rains of which little is known about their movements during the off-season. Two other species probably occur as migrant breeders though nesting has never been proved. Several species may be either resident or migrant; more work will have to be undertaken before their true status is known.

One species occurs in The Gambia as a passage visitor from the southern hemisphere, Wilson's Petrel *Oceanites oceanicus*, reported off Banjul and in the estuary of the river in recent years during April–May, on northward migration from its Antarctic and sub-Antarctic breeding grounds. Four species can best be described as oceanic wanderers. Four Nearctic vagrants have been reported.

Palaearctic Passage and Winter Visitors

Nearly a quarter of the species on the Gambian list are birds which breed in Europe, many of them in the far north of the continent, and migrate south in late summer and autumn to spend the winter in sub-Saharan Africa.

The first arrivals are surprisingly early. Flocks of Swifts *Apus apus* pass along the coast from late June and continue to pass southwards until early October. The earliest arrivals are probably from Mediterranean and North African breeding colonies but northerly breeding waders start arriving in late July, the earliest dates being 25 July for Ruffs *Philomachus pugnax* and 30 July for Curlew Sandpipers *Calidris ferruginea*. These dates relate to flocks which had clearly arrived on migration and were not non-breeding birds which had over-summered in The Gambia, small numbers of which are present each year.

The main southerly migration is from mid-September until mid-November, with a peak in October. Obvious passage migrants at this time are Spotted and Pied Flycatchers *Muscicapa striata* and *Ficedula hypoleuca*, Olivaceous Warblers *Hippolais pallida*, Willow Warblers *Phylloscopus trochilus*, Whinchats *Saxicola rubetra*, Woodchat Shrikes *Lanius senator* and White and Yellow Wagtails *Motacilla alba* and *M. flava*. The large majority of passerines move further south to winter, only a few individuals remaining to over-winter but some, particularly Nightingales *Luscinia megarhynchos*, Redstarts *Phoenicurus phoenicurus* and Subalpine Warblers *Sylvia cantillans* over-winter in considerable numbers, *S. cantillans* being one of the very few species to utilise mangrove as an important habitat.

The spring migration from February to April, with a peak in mid-March, is less noticeable and it seems that the great majority of migrants overfly The Gambia on their northwards migration, presumably having built up sufficient fat resources to see them through their trans-Saharan journey amidst the lush vegetation further south. An exception, however, is the Turtle Dove *Streptopelia turtur*, which at times occurs in huge numbers in Middle River in March.

The Waders

The Gambia is an important passage and wintering ground for Palaearctic waders. It is difficult to say how many actually winter and how many stay for only a few days or weeks en route to and from their breeding grounds in northern Europe. The wintering range of most species extends over a considerable distance, some of them reaching South Africa. Within this range individuals probably have their regular wintering sites, just as they have regular nesting sites in Europe. The impression gained from observation in The Gambia is that those waders which arrive early in the autumn, in September and October, stay for only a short time and then move on further south, and that it is those which have left Europe much later or have taken longer on their journey which remain through the winter. Considerably more study is however required before this can be confirmed.

The most abundant of the waders to be seen on the mudflats in the vicinity of Banjul are Little Stints *Calidris minuta* and Curlew Sandpipers *C. ferruginea*. They are present from late July until mid-April with maximum numbers in September–October and March, clearly indicating that only a small percentage winter as far north as The Gambia. Flocks are still present on the northward spring migration at the end of April, occasionally in early May, and the first returning birds arrive back again in the last days of July. Knots *Calidris canutus* and Dunlin *C. alpina* also occur on the mudflats, but they are scarce and irregular, only occurring intermittently in small parties mainly during the migration periods. A few Bar-tailed Godwits *Limosa lapponica* are present on the flats, mostly at Cape Lagoon, throughout the winter months. They arrive in small flocks, but these soon break up and each bird appears to acquire its own territory and for the rest of the winter individuals are to be seen feeding singly on the tidal mudflats. Black-tailed Godwits *L. limosa* on the other hand remain in flocks and although small parties sometimes occur on the mudflats they are mainly found in the freshwater marshes and ricefields, often in mixed flocks with Ruffs *Philomachus pugnax*. The flocks occur throughout the country, becoming more concentrated as the dry season progresses and the marshes dry up.

The coastline mostly comprises sandy beaches and from August until April flocks of Sanderling *Calidris alba*, each numbering between 15–30 birds, are spaced out a few hundred yards apart along the length of the coast. It is not known whether any of the flocks remain for the whole winter on a chosen stretch of beach or whether there is a gradual movement southwards. Some birds undoubtedly remain in the same area for several months, as individual birds have been identified in separate flocks which remained on one stretch of beach for 2–3 months in November–January. It seems probable that the earlier flocks to arrive move further south, while birds which arrive later reach the southernmost point of their migration in The Gambia.

Two other waders occur only on the Atlantic coast. Flocks of Oyster-catchers *Haematopus ostralegus* begin arriving at the end of August, resting for a few days and then moving on; a familiar sight in the early morning in September and October is parties flying southwards 100 m or so offshore. Only a few individuals over-winter, mostly at Cape Lagoon.

Whereas migrating Grey Plovers *Pluvialis squatarola* travel in flocks, like the Bar-tailed Godwits, once they reach their wintering grounds they separate and individuals take up their own feeding 'territories' along the length of the beaches. The Grey Plovers which occur in The Gambia in September and October and again in March are usually in flocks; clearly they are birds which winter further south.

Turnstones *Arenaria interpres* are passage migrants, small parties occurring both on the beaches and the mudflats at the mouth of the river in October–November and March–April.

Except for the Little Ringed Plover *Charadrius dubius*, which occurs inland as a passage migrant mainly in November and March, the other small plovers are usually found on the coast, though they may occasionally occur along the banks of the river. Ringed and Kentish Plovers *C. hiaticula* and *C. alexandrinus* are normally seen in small flocks on passage, though a few over-winter, when they may be seen in company with Kittlitz's Sand-plover *C. pecuarius*, an intra-African migrant which is present in The Gambia during the off-season.

Like the two godwits, the closely-related Curlew and Whimbrel *Numenius arquata* and *N. phaeopus* occupy different habitats in their winter quarters and are rarely seen together. The Whimbrel is the most obvious of the waders for it feeds on dry open ground, often far from water and sometimes in the vicinity of villages. Football pitches and the golf course are favoured feeding grounds and individuals occur in the open fields inland of the sand-dunes down the length of the coast. Curlew favour the mudflats, and in particular the muddy creeks which meander through the mangrove swamps along the lower reaches of the river. Here, too, are found wintering Greenshanks and Redshanks *Tringa nebularia* and *T. totanus*, both of which winter in quite large numbers; the few Spotted Redshanks *Tringa erythropus* which visit on passage, mostly in the spring, also occur in these swamps. It is believed that somewhere along the lower reaches of the river there may be an as yet undiscovered wintering ground for Avocets *Recurvirostra avosetta*. They winter in neighbouring Senegal and flocks have been seen along the river, but to date no-one has located a wintering area in The Gambia.

Of the smaller sandpipers only the Marsh Sandpiper *Tringa stagnatalis* is normally found on the saline flats. A total of perhaps 20 over-winter in the vicinity of Banjul each year and a few more pass through on migration. Common Sandpipers *T. hypoleucos*, which are mainly passage migrants with a few individuals over-wintering, may be found wherever there is water from the coast to the upper reaches of the river. Wood and Green Sandpipers *T. glareola* and *T. ochropus* favour freshwater marshes. The former are common and are present in every swamp and ricefield throughout the country from September until April. The latter are less numerous and those which over-winter in The Gambia occur on inland marshes; they only appear on the coast during the migration seasons, often in small parties, clearly birds on passage to and from their wintering grounds further south. Another wader normally found inland, and only on migration, is Temminck's Stint *Calidris temminckii*; it is rare, but probably largely overlooked. Common Snipe *Gallinago gallinago* occur on freshwater swamps throughout the winter and Jack Snipe *G. minima* have been recorded as vagrants. Black-winged Stilts *Himantopus himantopus* are passage migrants, small parties being present mostly in November and March.

Intra-African Migrants

The 23 regular dry season visitors appear to be birds which breed inland and probably further north in the Sahel during the short rains and move to the coast and the borders of the larger rivers to spend the off-season. They include some of the most brilliantly coloured birds to be seen in West Africa; 3 species of bee-eater, the Blue-cheeked *Merops superciliosus* (possibly a migrant from Morocco, so that it could be classified as a Palaearctic migrant), Carmine *M. nubicus* and White-throated *M. albicollis*; and the Abyssinian Roller *Coracias abyssinica*, a common and noticeable dry season visitor from November until May which can be seen perched on telephone wires along every roadside, or swooping through the smoke above bush fires to catch insects escaping from the flames.

Other visitors during the dry season are Grasshopper Buzzards *Butastur rufipennis*, which occur commonly in Middle and Upper River but only occasionally on the coast; Crocodile Birds *Pluvianus aegyptius*, along the upper reaches of the river, particularly near Basse; Long-tailed Doves *Oena capensis* along every dusty track and roadside; Splendid Glossy Starlings *Lamprotornis splendidus* in forest; and Cut-throats *Amadina fasciata* in open scrubland.

Eight species are known to be migrant breeders arriving just before the start of the rains, mostly in May, and departing after breeding. Most leave immediately after the end of the rains, sometimes earlier, but the 2 storks remain into the dry season until March when their young fledge. The migrant breeders are: Marabou Storks *Leptoptilos crumeniferus*, Wood Ibis *Ibis ibis*, Levaillant's Cuckoo *Clamator levaillantii*, Didric Cuckoo *Chrysococcyx caprius*, Pigmy Kingfisher *Ceyx picta*, Senegal Kingfisher *Halcyon senegalensis*, Nigerian Little Bunting *Emberiza forbesi* and Rock Bunting *E. tahapisi*. Their movements outside the breeding season are not known, but the 2 storks almost certainly move south along the coast to wetter areas to spend the 3–4 months they are away from The Gambia.

ACKNOWLEDGEMENTS

First Edition

I should firstly like to express my gratitude to Dr J. F. Monk who, as editor, has shown immense patience during the preparation of this Check-list and whose constantly sound advice has been invaluable.

I should also like to thank the past and present Chairmen and committee members of The Gambia Ornithological Society for their support and advice and in particular C. V. Eyre OBE and Dr M. E. Smalley, current Chairman and Recorder of the Society respectively, for reading and commenting on the species notes which constitute the main part of the Check-list.

I am grateful to Drs P. Colston and D. W. Snow of the Bird Room, British Museum (Natural History) at Tring for their help in identifying certain species from photographs and skins, and the staff of the Bird Room for their assistance during my visits there; Dr P. Evans of The Edward Grey Institute of Ornithology for his assistance in compiling the References; and E. M. Cawkell for kindly making available to me a copy of an unpublished paper on the birds of The Gambia which he had prepared in collaboration with Mrs D. Bray.

Last, but by no means least, I should like to thank my wife who accompanied me on most of my travels in The Gambia and who has accepted without complaint the mass of drafts, papers and references which for so long have covered the greater part of our joint study.

Second Edition

I should like to take this opportunity to thank Chris White, the Chairman of The Gambia Ornithological Society since 1978, Peter Byass, Recorder 1984–89, Dr

Derek Clifford, present Recorder and Clive Barlow, a professional ornithologist who has lived in Fajara since 1985, for all the help and advice which they gave me during my return visits to The Gambia in March and October 1989. I also wish to express my appreciation to all those individuals whose names appear in parentheses in the systematic list, for supplying me with records post-1980, to the new editor of the series, Dr Llewellyn Grimes, for his helpful and constructive advice and last, but by no means least, to my long-suffering secretary, Susan Farrent, for typing the manuscript, who together have enabled me to bring this new edition up to date.

SYSTEMATIC LIST

In the Systematic List the sequence of families and sub-families follows Morony, Bock & Farrand's (1975) widely used '*Reference Lists of the Birds of the World*'. Genera are arranged alphabetically within families or sub-families and species alphabetically within genera. Scientific nomenclature follows White's (1960–65) *Revised Check-list of African Birds* with Bannerman's (1930–51) names in brackets where these differ. In a few cases recently accepted changes in nomenclature have been used with the previous names in brackets. Sub-species are included where known and follow White. English names are those of Serle *et al.* (1977). In cases where there are alternative and widely-used English names, e.g. in Bannerman (1930–51) and Mackworth-Praed & Grant (1970–73), these are included in brackets.

General statements on status are based on information contained in the following: Bannerman (1930–51) and in his shorter 2 volume work (1953); Cawkell & Moreau (1963) (referred to as Cawkell & Moreau); Cawkell (1965); Bray, Mulholland & Vittery (1966) (= Bray *et al.*) with Addenda 1967 and 1969; Morel (1972); Morel & Morel (in prep.); The Gambia Ornithological Society's Revision of Bray *et al.* (1975) (= GOS Rev); the Annual Bird Reports of The Gambia Ornithological Society 1975–81 and 1986–87 (= GOS ABR 1975–81, 1986–87); the Rarities Report 1982–86 (= GOS RR); the Gambian–German Forestry Project report (= GGFP); and Jensen & Kirkeby (1980). Unpublished personal observations and communications are indicated by giving the initials of the individual in front of the surname.

The following abbreviations have been used as an indication of status:

RB	Resident breeder
MB	Migrant breeder
FB	Former breeder
PV	Palaearctic passage visitor
WV	Palaearctic winter visitor
DSV	Dry season visitor (intra-African migrant)
WSV	Wet season visitor (intra-African migrant)
AfM	Intra-African migrant (season unspecified)
AV	Accidental or casual visitor of up to 10 records

Brackets indicate that the status is variable or irregular; a question mark that the status is uncertain or unknown, but does not question occurrence; e.g. (PV) = irregular passage visitor; ?RB = status uncertain, possibly resident breeder; RB? = probably resident but breeding uncertain. An asterisk indicates that breeding is almost certain but has never been proved. The entries for 11 species whose occurrence is not considered by the writer to be authenticated are placed in square brackets while 19 species are rejected.

I have used 6 terms to try to give a general indication of the degree of abundance of each species, defined as follows:

Abundant	—invariably encountered, when present in their normal habitat, in large numbers as residents or visitors.
Common	—invariably encountered singly (e.g. birds of prey) or in quite good numbers in their normal habitat
Not uncommon	—usually, but not invariably, encountered in their normal habitat.
Uncommon	—fairly frequently, but not regularly, encountered in their normal habitat.

Scarce —only irregularly and infrequently encountered in their normal habitat.
Rare —rarely encountered.

For the purpose of this List the country has been divided into 4 sections, which have no administrative or geographical basis. The Coast (Fig. 1) covers offshore waters, the mouth of the River Gambia (including the capital Banjul) and the beaches. Lower River (Fig. 1) covers from Banjul inland to Tendaba, Middle River (Fig. 2) from Tendaba to Georgetown and Upper River (Fig. 3) covers from Georgetown to the eastern border of the country.

NON-PASSERIFORMES

PODICIPEDIDAE

[PODICEPS CRISTATUS

Great Crested Grebe

Bannermans's inclusion of this species (Bannerman 1930–51) is apparently based on a sight record by Hopkinson of a large grebe off MacCarthy I. in Mar 1902. Cawkell & Moreau considered its occurrence unlikely even as a straggler, though later one was photographed at Djoudj in northern Senegal, 20 Jan 1971 (Morel 1972).]

1. PODICEPS (=POLIOCEPHALUS) RUFICOLLIS DSV, (MB)

Dabchick (or Little Grebe)

Regular visitor (*P.r. capensis*) in the dry season, Nov–Jul. Recorded annually in small numbers throughout the dry season near the pumping station along Banjul Bund and at Kotu sewage farm, occasionally elsewhere inland to Kai Hai I. Maximum 12 at sewage farm early Jul 1989; one pair attempted to breed but the nest was flooded — the first breeding record (C. R. Barlow). Breeds at Richard Toll in Senegal (Morel 1972).

[PROCELLARIIDAE

There are no records of any members of this family from Gambian waters though 5 species have been recorded out to sea off Senegal (Morel and Morel in prep.). Cory's Shearwater *Procellaria diomedea* is common in winter further south along the West African coast and must occur off The Gambia; other species which have been recorded in Senegal and are likely to occur but have been overlooked are Little Shearwater *P. assimilis*, Great Shearwater *P. gravis*, Sooty Shearwater *P. grisea* and Manx Shearwater *P. puffinus*.]

HYDROBATIDAE

2. HYDROBATES LEUCORHOA AV

Leach's Petrel

Palaearctic vagrant; only record is one observed off the coast, 2 Sep 1967 (Morel 1972).

3. HYDROBATES PELAGICUS PV, WV

Storm Petrel

Seen regularly by Cawkell in the estuary, May–Jul (Cawkell & Moreau), non-breeders over-summering. Bourne (*Ibis* (1963) 105: 407) suggests the records relate to *O. oceanicus*, but Cawkell (1965) knew both species during 6 years in the Falkland Is. Few records since but probably regular and not uncommon out to sea in winter, but overlooked. Several (no number given) were present in the estuary in Jun 1966 (Bray *et al.*), single off Fajara, 12 Feb 1983 and *c.* 100 off Barra, 30 Jan 1984 (GOS RR). One near Farafenni, 11 Feb 1988 (an unusual record), 2 near Dog I., 9 Feb 1988 and several in the estuary 24 Feb 1988 (G. Rainey).

4. OCEANITES OCEANICUS (PV)

Wilson's Petrel

Scarce and irregular passage visitor (from the southern winter). First recorded in 1965 when there were 66 records in the estuary off Banjul, Apr–Jun and Aug–Sep (Bray *et al.*). No further records until *c.* 20 were seen 27 Apr 1975; thereafter flocks of up to 30 regularly observed close-in off Government Wharf on most days to 9 May when *c.* 62 were seen in parties of up to 12 between Banjul Wharf and Buoy No 2 (GOS ABR 1975). In 1977 *c.* 50 were counted from Banjul-Barra ferry, 16 Apr and *c.* 5 off Banjul Wharf, 20 Apr (GOS ABR 1977). No records since.

[OCEANODROMA CASTRO Rejected

Madeiran Petrel

Included in brackets by Jensen & Kirkeby (1980) as occurring off the coast, but there are no Gambian records.]

PHAETHONTIDAE

[PHAETHON LEPTURUS Rejected

White-tailed Tropicbird

Included in brackets by Jensen & Kirkeby (1980) from one possible 1973 record of 3 over Bakau. This record is not acceptable.]

PELECANIDAE

5. PELECANUS ONOCROTALUS DSV

White Pelican

Reported only in Lower River in the dry season when it is not uncommon. Most numerous in the Tankular-Tendaba area where flocks of up to 100 have been reported in Dec (GOS Rev). Occasionally seen with *P. rufescens* off Banjul Bund. Six observed Aug 1963 in large tree in Kwinella in which *P. rufescens* nests (Cawkell 1965), but there is no evidence of breeding.

6. PELECANUS RUFESCENS RB

Pink-backed (or Grey) Pelican

Common resident in Lower and Middle River. The main known breeding colony, estimated *c.* 70 pairs in 1987, in 3 trees in Kwinella, has been occupied for several years. Other smaller colonies occur near Dog I. and at Jappeni (established 1987), and doubtless there are others adjoining the mangrove swamps. Breeds Sep–Jan.

SULIDAE

7. SULA (=MORUS) BASSANA — WV

Gannet

Regular winter visitor (*S.b. bassana*) in small numbers off the coast, mostly immatures. Most records are Nov–Mar, but over-summering birds recorded; immature found injured (later died) at Cape St Mary, 5 Jul 1976 (GOS ABR 1976); one ringed as fledgling on Bass Rock, off East Lothian, Scotland on 8 Jul 1975 found dead at Gunjur, May 1978 (M. E. Smalley); another Bass Rock ringed bird was found dead 1984 (GOS RR). Largest number recorded (20 first winter birds) off Cape St Mary, 13 Jan 1983 (GOS RR). *S.b. capensis* is presumed not to range as far north as The Gambia.

8. SULA LEUCOGASTER — AV

Brown Booby

The only records are one (*S.l. leucogaster*) off the Gambian coast on 1 Jun 1969 (Morel 1972) and an adult at Fajara, 6 Jan 1975 (Jensen & Kirkeby 1980).

PHALACROCORACIDAE

9. PHALACROCORAX AFRICANUS — RB

Long-tailed Shag (or Cormorant)

Common resident on the coast and inland along the river. Breeding colonies are undoubtedly scattered on islands in the mangrove in Lower and Middle River, but only two are known: at Niani Maru — 200–300 pairs present Jul 1969 (GOS Rev) — and at Baboon I. National Park Nov 1987 and Nov 1988 (J. N. Dymond). Numbers increase near the coast after the rains, indicating post-breeding dispersal.

10. PHALACROCORAX CARBO (=LUCIDUS) — DSV

White-breasted (or African) Cormorant

Mainly a not uncommon dry season visitor (*P.c. lucidus*) in small numbers on the coast, usually seen perched on masts of derelict ground-nutters and other wrecks off Banjul Bund. Some occur inland to Middle River. Has been recorded in most months, but no evidence of breeding. Nearest known colonies are in the delta of the Senegal River and in Casamance (Morel 1972).

ANHINGIDAE

11. ANHINGA RUFA — RB

African Darter (or Snake Bird)

Common resident (*A.r. rufa*) in Lower and Middle River. Only known breeding colonies are at Niani Maru — less than 30 pairs present Aug 1969 (GOS Rev) — and Baboon I. National Park, but doubtless others exist along the river.

FREGATIDAE

12. FREGATA MAGNIFICENS AV

Magnificent Frigate Bird

Oceanic vagrant; Bannerman (1930–51) states that it has been taken in The Gambia but gives no details. Only 2 recent records: a female observed off Government Wharf, Banjul, 24 Mar 1965 (Bray *et al.*); 2 off Cape St Mary, 18 Oct 1980 (GOS ABR 1980).

ARDEIDAE
Botaurinae

13. BOTAURUS STELLARIS AV

Bittern

Vagrant from the Palaearctic, only 2 records: one at Kotu Stream, 22 Feb 1974 (Jensen & Kirkeby 1980); one flying over Mandinari, 12 Apr 1977 (GOS ABR 1977). There is also a doubtful record of one at Banjul Bund, 21 Nov 1963 (Bray *et al.*). Rarely seen in West Africa.

14. IXOBRYCHUS MINUTUS RB, ?WV

Little Bittern

Rare resident (*I.m. payesii*); probably also winter visitor (*I.m. minutus*) from the Palaearctic. Recorded from Camaloo, 3 May 1965, 4 May 1966, Jan 1972 (GOS Rev), 18n Apr 1977 (GOS ABR 1977), Feb 1980 (GOS ABR 1980); Georgetown, 11 Oct 1966 (GOS Rev); Upper River, Jan 1983; Wallikunda, Jul 1985 and Tendaba, Nov 1985 (GOS RR); Marakissa, Aug 1989 (C. R. Barlow). Nest with one egg at Camaloo, 7 Sep 1962 (Bray, *et al.*) is the only breeding record.

15. IXOBRYCHUS (=ARDEIRALLUS) STURMII RB?

Dwarf Bittern

Probably a scarce resident in mangrove in Lower and Middle River (twice recorded Upper River) but status uncertain; though seen in all months there are no breeding records. Single birds at different times at Camaloo, Abuko, Kotu Stream, Yundum and Elephant I.; pair seen regularly near Bansang, Aug–Nov 1979 (GOS ABR 1979) and single at Basse, 16 Sep 1980 (GOS ABR 1980).

[TIGRIORNIS LEUCOLOPHUS Rejected

Tiger Bittern

The record of one at Tendaba, 25 Nov 1982 included in Morel & Morel (in prep.) was not accepted (GOS RR).]

Ardeinae

16. ARDEA CINEREA WV, AfM

Grey Heron

Locally common Palaearctic winter visitor (*A.c. cinerea*), and intra-African migrant (*A.c. monicae*) Sep–Mar, on fresh-water swamps; most numerous on the coast and in Lower River; scarce further inland. Some non-breeding birds remain throughout the year. No breeding colonies have been located and there is no evidence to suggest that any are resident breeders.

17. ARDEA (=TYPHON) GOLIATH RB

Goliath Heron

Resident and not uncommon in mangrove along Lower and Middle River; scarce on the coast. Undoubtedly breeds, but no recent records. Two birds in the Zoological Gardens in London were taken in The Gambia from a nest on the ground on a small dry island among mangroves (Bannerman 1930–51).

18. ARDEA MELANOCEPHALA MB, AfM

Black-headed Heron

Widespread and not uncommon, mainly dry season visitor, though there are records through the rains; numbers decrease as the wet season progresses and southward movement has been observed along the coast, Nov–Dec (GOS Rev, GOS ABR 1977). Breeding recorded Apr–Jun (Bannerman 1930–51); juveniles seen Jul–Sep (Cawkell & Moreau), but few colonies now known. A mixed heronry established in the middle of Basse town post 1980 contained several pairs, Aug 1987 (C. R. Barlow). Nest building at Abuko Nature Reserve, Nov 1987 (C. R. Barlow).

ARDEA (=PYRRHERODIA) PURPUREA RB*, WV

Purple Heron

Scarce resident (*A.p. purpurea*), mostly in Lower River; numbers augmented, presumably by migrants from Europe, Sep–Mar. Breeding never proved, but pair behaving as if nesting at Camaloo, Feb–Mar 1976 (GOS ABR 1976). Breeds in Senegal Jun–Aug.

20. ARDEOLA (=BUBULCUS) IBIS RB

Cattle Egret (or Buff-backed Heron)

Common resident (*A.i. ibis*) accompanying most herds of cattle. The many flocks of 15–30 flighting to roost by the river at dusk are one of the sights of The Gambia. Breeds Jul–Sep in the rains in colonies scattered throughout the country, mostly in Silk Cotton trees, *Bombax costatum* and *B. buonopozense*.

21. ARDEOLA RALLOIDES RB, WV

Squacco Heron

Resident, widely distributed and not uncommon in freshwater swamps throughout the country; numbers augmented by Palaearctic immigrants, Oct–Mar. Breeds Jul–Sep; largest known colony 150–200 pairs at Niani Maru.

22. BUTORIDES STRIATUS RB

Green-backed Heron

Resident and not uncommon (*B.s. atricapillus*) in wetlands and mangrove in Lower River and inland at forest edge along the length of the river, particularly along overgrown creeks. Numbers appear to have increased since 1984, doubtless as a result of heavier rainfall. Breeds Aug–Nov, sometimes into Dec, C/2–3.

23. EGRETTA (=CASMERODIUS) ALBA RB

Great White Egret (or Heron)

Common resident (*E.a. melanorhynchos*) in Lower and Middle River. Several breeding colonies of 20–100 pairs in Middle River, mostly in large trees in the centre of villages; breeding in association with Buffalo Weavers *Bubalornis albirostris* often occurs, the herons' nests frequently being on top and part of the nests of the weavers. Breeds Jul–Dec.

24. EGRETTA (=MELANOPHOYX) ARDESIACA RB, DSV

Black Heron

Locally common resident in Lower and Middle River; also local migrant as numbers increase during the dry season: up to 35 at Camaloo, Mar–Apr 1977 (GOS ABR 1977), 30 at Mara Kissa, Feb 1989 and 40 there, 25 Mar 1989 (C. R. Barlow). Largest flock reported, 70–80 at Kaiaff, Jan 1974 (GOS Rev). Only breeding record is C/3 (at date and site unknown) (BMNH) but several present at mixed colony at Baboon I. National Park, Nov 1987 and Nov 1988, though none actually seen at nests (J. N. Dymond). Six birds pairing at Kotu Stream, Jun 1966 (Bray *et al.*).

25. EGRETTA GARZETTA RB, WV

Little Egret

Not uncommon resident; numbers augmented by winter visitors from southern Europe, Oct–Mar. Bird ringed in the Camargue, France recovered in The Gambia in Feb (Morel & Roux 1966). Most known breeding colonies are in Middle River; nest building at Jappeni, 27 Jul 1973; colony in tree over market-place at Kaur, 24 June 1974 (GOS Rev); colony at Baboon I. National Park, 1987–88. Dispersal along the river and to the coast occurs after breeding.

26. EGRETTA (=DEMIGRETTA) GULARIS RB

Reef Heron

Previously considered to be a race of *E. garzetta* and treated as such in 1st Edition but now generally accepted as being a distinct species. Common resident on the coast and inland along The River to the Trans-Gambia crossing (Fig. 2). Rare further inland, but 3 seen separately at Bansang, 7 Nov 1979 (GOS ABR 1979). Breeds during the rains Jul–Oct, juveniles appearing on the marshes in Sep. Breeding colonies are normally in trees immediately behind the mangroves; only known colony today is near Dog Island.

27. EGRETTA (=MESOPHOYX) INTERMEDIA RB, DSV

Yellow-billed Egret

Scarce resident and dry season visitor (*E.i. brachyrhyncha*). Most records are from Dec to May in Lower River, but has been recorded in all months at Camaloo. Breeds in Middle River; several pairs at nest in mixed colony at Baboon I. National Park, Nov 1987 and Nov 1988 (J. N. Dymond). Thirty with other egrets at Jakhaly, 10 Feb 1987 (GOS ABR 1986–87).

28. NYCTICORAX LEUCONOTUS RB

White-backed Night Heron

Rare local resident, previously possibly largely overlooked but numbers may have increased since 1984 with the onset of higher rainfall as it has been reported regularly since then. First recorded at Kotu Stream, 22 Apr and again there early Aug 1963 (Cawkell 1966) and Jul 1984 (B. K. Wright). Several records from Abuko Nature Reserve: singles 27 Aug 1977 (GOS ABR 1977), 26 Feb 1984, 4 Aug 1985 (GOS RR), May 1988 (C. White), 28 Nov 1988 (J. N. Dymond). There are several recent breeding records: P/2 in nest (adult photographed) near Tendaba 7 Aug 1984 (B. K. Wright); P/1 Abuko Nature Reserve, 6 Oct 1989; C/3 near Brikama, 8 Oct 1989 and 2 other nests, contents not examined, within 6 km radius of Brikama, 8 Oct 1989 (C. R. Barlow, M. E. J. Gore).

29. NYCTICORAX NYCTICORAX RB, WV

Night Heron

Resident and locally common (*N.n. nycticorax*); most numerous along the river bank in Middle and Upper River, but regular in Abuko Nature Reserve and appears to nest in or near the Reserve though the colony has not been located. Numbers augmented by migrants from southern Europe Oct–Mar; a bird ringed at Tam-et-Garonne, France, 15 Jun 1961 was found dead at Sintet, 15 Mar 1962 (Cawkell 1965). Only breeding record is from Niani Maru, where there were 20–40 pairs Jul–Sep 1966 (Bray *et al.*). Juveniles are common and colonies certainly exist today.

SCOPIDAE

30. SCOPUS UMBRETTA RB

Hammerkop

Resident and common, usually in the vicinity of fresh water throughout the country. Nest building and breeding extends throughout the year.

CICONIIDAE

31. CICONIA (=SPHENORHYNCHUS) ABDIMII (AfM)

Abdim's (or White-bellied) Stork

Rare and irregular visitor today. Only 4 recent records: 2 at Fattatenda, 13 Jul 1959 (Cawkell 1965); 2 near Albreda, 16 Apr 1972 (Jensen & Kirkeby 1980); one at Yundum, 8 Jul 1973 (GOS Rev) and one over the river near Kaur, 5 Mar 1976 (GOS ABR 1976). Bannerman (1930–51), however, described it as a regular visitor (not known to breed) in the wet season, from about May to Oct or Nov.

32. CICONIA CICONIA AV

White Stork

Only 4 definite records: one (location unspecified), 14 Apr 1970 (Morel 1972); one circling over a bushfire at Sapu, 31 Jan 1975 (GOS ABR 1975); 5 near Bansang, 11 Dec 1979 (P. Goll) and 2 on North Bank, Lower River, 30 Dec 1980 (GOS ABR 1980). Five flying over Mansakonko, 22 Sep 1964 (Bray *et al.*), were probably this species.

33. CICONIA (= DISSOURA) EPISCOPUS RB*

White-necked Stork

Scarce, probably resident, reported in all months, mostly inland in Lower River and Middle River, and may well breed (*C.e. microscelis*), but there are no records. Pairs and up to 5 together regularly reported from marshes at Tankular and Tendaba, Brumen Bridge (max 12 on 28 Sep 1979, 6 there 1 Oct 1989 (G. Rainey)) and Mansakonko; flock of 16 seen from river near Elephant I., Jan 1972 (GOS Rev); 11 separately along Middle River, 15 Jan 1975 (GOS ABR 1975).

34. CICONIA NIGRA AV

Black Stork

African, possibly Palaearctic, vagrant, the only accepted record is one at Upper Niumi in Nov 1923 (Bannerman 1930–51). There are two recent possible sightings but insufficient details were supplied by the observers for them to be accepted: singles in Upper River, Jan 1980 (GOS ABR 1980) and Jan 1984 (GOS RR).

35. EPHIPPIORHYNCHUS SENEGALENSIS ?RB

Saddlebill Stork (or Jabiru)

Considered resident but rare by Hopkinson from MacCarthy I. to the sea; 'usually seen singly but once a flock of a dozen appeared' (Bannerman 1930–51). Individuals seen only occasionally in various places (Cawkell 1965), since when only 5 records: an immature over Banjul, 7 Jan 1972 (GOS Rev); one near Sapu, 2 Feb 1975 (GOS ABR 1975); one at Banjul Bund, 19 Feb 1976 (Jensen & Kirkeby 1980); one Sapu, 28 Feb 1988 (G. Rainey) and one (photographed) at Tendaba, Jan 1988 (G. Langsbury). Breeds in Ghana and Ivory Coast, Oct–Dec (Grimes 1987).

36. IBIS IBIS MB

Wood Ibis (or Yellow-billed Stork)

Locally common breeding visitor to Middle River. Only two known breeding colonies today, *c.* 50 nests in one tree in the centre of Jappeni village, present at least since 1973, occupied Sep–Mar and *c.* 50 nests at Farafenni, Nov 1986 (J. N. Dymond). Other colonies almost certainly exist; 6 were known to Cawkell in 1961 (Cawkell & Moreau), the largest ones at Toniataba (*c.* 50 nests) and Barokunda (50 nests), though neither is now occupied. Cawkell reported that colony sites may be occupied for no more than 2–3 years, but may be re-occupied after another few years. Individuals and small parties occur near the coast mostly Feb–May and Aug–Sep when dispersal occurs out of breeding season.

37. LEPTOPTILOS CRUMENIFERUS MB

Marabou Stork

Locally common breeding visitor to Middle and Upper River. About 40 colonies of 5–12 pairs each, in Baobab trees *Adansonia digita* along the south bank road between Jappeni and Bansang, are occupied Oct–Mar. During post-breeding dispersal small parties occur on the coast, most birds probably moving south into Casamance, Senegal.

THRESKIORNITHIDAE
Threskiornithinae

38. BOSTRYCHIA (=HAGEDASHIA) HAGEDASH RB*

Hadada Ibis

Resident (*B.h. brevirostris*) in small numbers and not uncommon in Middle and Upper River east of Kaur, though there are no breeding records. Maximum reported are 17 along the river between Georgetown and Basse, Jan 1975 and 23 between Kaur and Sapu, Mar 1976 (GOS ABR 1975–76). Singles or small parties occasionally reported from Lower River, and on marshes near Banjul, mostly in the early part of the dry season, Nov–Mar, when some dispersal has occurred after breeding, which is presumably during the rains, Jul–Nov. Recent records of individuals from Abuko Nature Reserve, Feb–May 1987 and Tanji, 1988 (C. R. Barlow).

39. PLEGADIS FALCINELLUS PV, WV

Glossy Ibis

Bannerman (1930–51) records it from The Gambia but gives no details. Not mentioned for The Gambia by Serle *et al.* (1977) but data overlooked. First reported in 1959 (Cawkell 1965). Today it is a scarce passage and winter visitor in small numbers, a few being seen most years. Maximum numbers: 25 at Sapu, 9 Nov 1975 (GOS ABR 1975); 36 near Brikama, 16 Sep 1979 (GOS ABR 1979); 15 Middle River, 10 Jan 1984; flocks regularly reported in region of Kuntaur, max. 63 at Kudang, 29 Feb 1988 (G. Rainey).

40. THRESKIORNIS AETHIOPICA RB

Sacred Ibis

Scarce resident (*T.a. aethiopica*). Formerly bred on the Bijilo Is. where Moore counted 9 nests, Jul 1948 (Cawkell & Moreau). Two young were taken from a nest at Niani Maru, Dec 1962 (Bray *et al.*); only breeding colony now known is at Baboon I. National Park: 20+ pairs present, many on nests, Nov 1987 (J. N. Dymond). Flocks of up to 50 occur in Middle and Upper River; total of *c.* 150 counted along Middle River, Jan 1975 and *c.* 70 there, Mar 1976 (GOS ABR 1975–76). Individuals or small parties occur intermittently near the coast during the dry season, Nov–Jun.

41. PLATALEA ALBA RB, AfM

African Spoonbill

Rare resident and scarce dry season visitor presumably from the colonies in the delta of the Senegal River. Most records are during the early part of the dry season, Dec–Mar, but has been seen in all months on the mudflats off Banjul Bund and elsewhere in Lower and Middle River, singly or in parties of up to 8 (once 11) (Cawkell & Moreau, Cawkell 1965, Bray *et al.*, Morel 1972, GOS ABR 1975–76–77). Breeding first reported Baboon I. National Park, Nov 1987; at least 3 birds in full breeding plumage including displaying pair in mixed colony with *Threskiornis aethiopica* (J. N. Dymond).

42. PLATALEA LEUCORODIA AV

European Spoonbill

Vagrant from the Palaearctic, only 7 records: 2 on a brackish channel near Banjul, 19 Jan 1961, which remained until 12 Mar, 3 present on 24 Feb (Cawkell & Moreau); 2 at Tendaba, 30 Nov 1982; singles Banjul Bund, 1 and 14 Jan and 14 Mar 1984 and an adult and an immature there, Feb 1986 (GOS RR); one photographed at Kotu sewage farm, 25 Feb 1984 (C. White). A flock of 17 spoonbills flying along Bijilo beach at sunset, 6 Sep 1975, may have been this species (GOS ABR 1975).

PHOENICOPTERIDAE

43, PHOENICOPTERUS (=PHOENICONAIS) MINOR AV

Lesser Flamingo

Rare African vagrant, one sick bird found on the beach at Fajara in Mar 1982 survived for several days; the first confirmed record — presumably a straggler from the breeding colony in Mauritania. Since then small parties regularly reported in Lower River including 11 (photographed) in a mixed flock with *P. ruber* near Sika, Nov 1987 (G. Rainey). The identification of a flock of 200 flamingos flying over the river near Tendaba on 7 Mar 1974 as *P. minor*, described as being conspicuously deep red with fast wing beats (GOS Rev), remains doubtful.

44. PHOENICOPTERUS RUBER (WV), (AfM)

Greater Flamingo

Today a fairly regular winter visitor (*P.r. roseus*) to the estuary and inland along the mudflats in Lower River, most records being late Aug–Sep; Cawkell saw them occasionally in winter, usually singly but once 15; 100+ near James I., 9 Sep 1948 (Cawkell & Moreau). More recent records are *c.* 100 flying up-river at Mile 3 on 20 Aug 1966 (Bray *et al.*), 2 off Banjul Bund, 4–14 Nov 1968 (GOS Rev), 12 over the river at Sambang, 2 May 1976 (A. Moore). Three near Barra, 11 Nov and 9 Dec 1981, were presumably Palaearctic migrants (GOS ABR 1981). Sightings of *c.* 200 at Brumen Bridge, 5 Aug 1980 (GOS ABR 1980), *c.* 40 off Bund Road on 5 Jun, *c.* 25 near Denton Bridge, 12 Jun and again off Bund Road on 16 Jun 1981 suggest off-season flocks of African origin. Regularly seen since 1982 in small numbers up-river from James I. (G. Rainey). Unidentified flamingos seen Jan and Feb 1975 (GOS Rev), Apr 1976 (GOS ABR 1986) and 21 off Banjul Bund, 13 Dec 1979 were probably this species.

ANATIDAE
Anserinae — Dendrocygnini

45. DENDROCYGNA BICOLOR (=FULVA) AV

Fulvous Tree-duck

Six authenticated records only: 6 in Middle River in company with *c.* 5000 *A. querquedula* and *c.* 2000 *D. viduata* in late Feb 1973 ((GOS Rev); 2 near Kaur, 19 Feb 1974 (Jensen & Kirkeby 1980); 5 or 6 along Middle River, 31 Dec 1980 (GOS ABR 1980); one with a mixed flock of ducks near Baboon I. National Park, 27 Feb 1988 (G. Rainey); 23 at Tendaba, 22 Nov 1988; one at Georgetown, 24 Nov 1988 (J. N. Dymond). There was doubt about the 1973 record but full details have been supplied by the observers (J. N. Dymond & M. Wright).

46. DENDROCYGNA VIDUATA RB

White-faced Tree-duck

Common resident in Lower and Middle River with flocks of *c.* 500 at Kaiaff and Jakhaly swamps during the dry season. Breeds in freshwater marshes during the rains, Jul–Oct; C/10 at Kotu sewage farm, Aug 1989; chicks seen Sep and early Nov. Numbers appear to have increased since 1985 with improved rainfall.

Anatinae — Tadornini

47. ALOPOCHEN AEGYPTIACA AV

Egyptian Goose

Today a rare vagrant, numbers having diminished. In the early part of the century Hopkinson reported it not uncommon Jun–Dec, departing with its young about Dec (Bannerman 1930–51); Cawkell (1965) found it far less numerous, apparently only in the swamps near Batelling. Only 4 recent records: 25 between Mansakonko and Kaur, Dec 1965 (Bray *et al.*); an unrecorded number between Georgetown and Bansang, 17 Dec 1967 (GOS Rev); small flocks along Upper River, Dec 1984 and near Baboon I. National Park, Dec 1985 (GOS RR).

Anatinae — Cairinini

48. NETTAPUS AURITUS RB

Pigmy Goose

Scarce resident on freshwater marshes mostly in Middle River. Breeds in the rains Jul–Oct; chicks seen at Jakhaly, 8 Dec 1974 (GOS Rev) and pair with 5 fully fledged young there, 14 Jan 1978 (M. E. J. Gore). Dispersal occurs after breeding and pairs or small parties then often occur near the coast; probably most migrate south into Casamance or beyond during the dry season, but nothing is known of their movements.

49. PLECTROPTERUS GAMBENSIS RB

Spur-winged Goose

Common resident on freshwater marshes and along the river in Middle and Upper River; smaller numbers occur in Lower River, occasionally on the coast. Breeds during the rains; eggs and young found in Upper River, Oct–Nov.

50. SARKIDIORNIS MELANOTA DSV

Knob-billed Goose

Common dry season visitor (*S.m. melanota*) to inland marshes with flocks of up to 1000 formerly recorded at Jakhaly in Mar. No firm evidence that it breeds, though young birds have been shot Jan–Feb (GOS Rev).

Anatinae — Anatini

51. ANAS (=DAFILA) ACUTA (WV)

Pintail

Uncommon and irregular winter visitor (*A.a. acuta*), usually in small numbers, along Lower and Middle River. During his stay Hopkinson encountered it only once (Bannerman 1930–51). In the 1970s the following numbers were reported: 100–200 recorded Jan 1972 and Jan and Mar 1974; *c.* 1000 Dec–Jan 1973–74 (GOS Rev); only 3 in 1975 (GOS ABR 1975); none in 1976 or 1977; 9 in Apr 1978 (C. V. & J. Eyre) but 600 near Kudang, 16 Dec 1979 (R. Hume, D. Fisher). Reported as uncommon but seen regularly in Middle River since 1980 (GOS ABR 1986–87).

52. ANAS (=SPATULA) CLYPEATA (WV)

Shoveler

Scarce and irregular winter visitor, most records being from Middle River. Hopkinson saw it occasionally (Bannerman 1930–51). The only recent records are: a pair shot at Kaiaff, 20 Jan 1969; 2 in Middle River, Feb 1973 (J. N. Dymond & M. Wright); *c.* 10 near Tendaba, Dec 1973; several at Pakalinding, Feb–Mar 1974; one shot at Jakhaly, autumn 1974 (GOS Rev); 2 at Sambang, 23 Feb 1975 (GOS ABR 1975); one at Camaloo, 2 Dec 1978 (M. E. Smalley) and 3 at Kotu sewage farm, Oct 1988 (C. R. Barlow). The unattributed record of *c.* 100 at Jakhaly swamp, Mar 1975 (GOS Rev) appears to be an error.

53. ANAS CRECCA WV

Teal

Rare Palaearctic visitor to West Africa, until recently only 3 records: 15 at Soma, 18 Dec 1973, a single there 10 Jan 1974 and 30 on the river (no location given), Jan 1974 (Jensen & Kirkeby 1980). Since 1985 one or 2 have been reported annually, Nov–Dec, at Kotu sewage farm.

54. ANAS PLATYRHYNCHOS AV

Mallard

Vagrant from the Palaearctic; Hopkinson reported it a common winter visitor, stating ‘many are shot for the pot’ (Bannerman 1930–51), but there is no recent record. Generally uncommon in West Africa.

55. ANAS QUERQUEDULA WV

Garganey

The only migrant Palaearctic duck which is abundant. Large numbers congregate east of Tendaba along Middle River, Dec–Mar. A few reported annually at Kotu sewage farm since 1985. Largest numbers recorded are: *c.* 1550 at Kaiaff, 12 Jan 1969; *c.* 4000 in same area Feb–Mar 1974 (GOS Rev); *c.* 300 on river below Bambatenda and several flocks which joined into one flock of *c.* 5000 above Elephant I., 6 Mar 1976, but only a single remained 3 weeks later (GOS ABR 1976). Present in thousands annually Feb–Mar, in Middle River, 1982–89 (G. Rainey).

Anatinae — Aythyini

56. AYTHYA (=NYROCA) FERINA AV

Pochard

Vagrant from the Palaearctic, only 3 records: *c.* 10 near Tendaba, Dec 1973; one by Banjul Bund, 16 Apr 1975 (GOS Rev); 4 near Kaur, 1 Dec 1988 (G. Rainey).

57. AYTHYA (=NYROCA) FULIGULA AV

Tufted Duck

Vagrant from the Palaearctic; Hopkinson reported that on 2 occasions he saw large flocks of 'black and white diving ducks which could be none other than this species' (Bannerman 1930–51). Andrews and Simms conducted annual duck counts 1967–69 and saw none. The only recent records are a single bird with a large mixed flocks of ducks near Sambang in Middle River, 25 Mar 1973 (J. N. Dymond & M. Wright), not in 1974 as stated in GOS Rev, and one near Kudang, 15 Feb 1988 (G. Rainey).

58. AYTHYA (=NYROCA) NYROCA AV

Ferruginous Duck (or White-eyed Pochard)

African vagrant, 4 records only: *c.* 20 in mixed flocks of ducks on river near Sambang, 23 Feb 1975 (GOS ABR 1975); one near Bansang on 1 Aug and 4 there on 17 Aug 1979 (P. Goll); a pair with a small flock of *A. acuta* near Carrol's Wharf, 29 Feb 1988 (G. Rainey). Omitted from The Gambia by Serle *et al.* who consider it uncommon west of northern Nigeria.

PANDIONIDAE

59. PANDION HALIAETUS WV

Osprey

Palaearctic visitor (*P.h. haliaetus*), Sep–Apr, on the coast and inland along the river to the Trans-Gambia crossing at Bambatenda. Rare further inland. The wintering population numbers 100–200. Non-breeders occasionally over-summer.

ACCIPITRIDAE
Aegypiinae

60. AEGYPIUS (=TORGOS) TRACHELIOTUS AV

Lappet-faced Vulture

African vagrant, only 5 records: singles near Basse in 1947 (no date given) (Cawkell & Moreau) and 24 Feb 1975 (GOS ABR 1975) and near Bwiam, 1 Oct 1962 (Cawkell & Moreau); 2 along Middle River, 14 Jan 1975 (GOS ABR 1975) and one there during the annual cattle drive at Kudang–Kuntaur, 23 Feb 1989 (T. Wacher).

61. GYPOHIERAX ANGOLENSIS RB

Palm-nut Vulture

Common on the coast and through Lower and Middle River and in Upper River to Bansang, less so further inland. One of the characteristic birds of The Gambia. Breeds Jan–Apr; eyries are known to have been occupied for many years, *viz* one in a rhun palm in the U.S. Ambassador's garden at Fajara since 1974 to the present (C. R. Barlow, M. E. J. Gore).

62. GYPS BENGALENSIS (=PSEUDOGYPS AFRICANUS) RB

White-backed vulture

Common resident (*G.b. africanus*) in open country; most numerous in Middle and Upper River, only small numbers occurring near the coast. Breeds Nov–Jun.

63. GYPS RUPPELLII RB

Ruppell's Griffon Vulture

Resident and not uncommon (*G.r. ruppellii*) in open country inland from about Bwiam; rare on the coast. Appears to be most numerous on the north bank east of Farafenni; it outnumbered both *G. bengalensis* and *N. monachus* at 2 dead cows several miles apart near Bambali, 7 May 1976 (GOS ABR 1976). Breeds after the rains, Dec–Mar; half-grown young in nest in tree near Keneba, 6 Mar 1975 (GOS Rev).

64. NEOPHRON (=NECROSYRTES) MONACHUS RB

Hooded Vulture

Abundant resident throughout the country; the common vulture of towns and villages. One hundred and thirty five counted circling and perched in trees around a dead warthog within 10 minutes of it being shot at Jakhaly, 10 May 1976 (M. E. J. Gore). Breeds Nov–Mar.

65. NEOPHRON PERCNOPTERUS AV

Egyptian Vulture

African vagrant, only 7 records (all singles): at Jassong, 3 Dec 1913 (Bannerman 1930–51); Fajara, 8 Mar 1962 (Cawkell & Moreau), 6 Jan 1981 in a mixed flock of vultures (GOS ABR 1981); Yundum, 24 Jun 1962 (Cawkell & Moreau); Banjul Bund, 24 Apr 1966 (Bray *et al.*); in Lower River (place unspecified) late Feb–early Mar 1973 (GOS Rev); Abuko, 14 Dec 1975 (GOS ABR 1975).

66. TRIGONOCEPS OCCIPITALIS RB

White-headed Vulture

Scarce resident in open country, usually seen singly or in pairs in Middle and Upper River; only occasionally reported from Lower River. Breeds Feb–Jun.

Circini

67. CIRCAETUS CINERASCENS RB*

Banded Harrier-eagle

Scarce resident in riverine and open forest in Middle and Upper River, but breeding has never been proved. Recorded along the river near Mansakonko, Jappeni, Kuntaur, Georgetown, Bansang and Basse, Nov–Mar. Only records from Lower River are singles at Brufut, 6 Mar 1965 (Bray *et al.*), Banjul in Nov 1968 (GOS Rev), Brumen Bridge, 15 Dec 1975 (GOS ABR 1975) and Tanji, Oct 1988 (C. R. Barlow).

68. CIRCAETUS CINEREUS RB*

Brown Harrier-eagle

Uncommon resident inland in open bush with scattered trees and on the edge of open forest; rare on the coast. Often seen perched high in tree in the middle of groundnut fields. Undoubtedly breeds, but no nest has been found.

69a. CIRCAETUS GALLICUS GALLICUS PV, WV

Short-toed Eagle

Regular but scarce Palaearctic passage and winter visitor, recorded between 17 Aug and 14 Apr. mostly Oct. Difficult to separate from *C.g. beaudouini* in the field. Winter records from Middle and Upper River, where *C.g. beaudouini* is resident, could relate to either species; but most seen in winter in Lower River, where *C.g. beaudouini* is rarely encountered, are probably *C. gallicus*.

69b. CIRCAETUS GALLICUS BEAUDOUINI RB*

Beaudouin's Harrier-eagle

Considered a distinct species in 1st edition *C. beaudouini* but now classed as a race of *C. gallicus*. Scarce resident in open country; almost certainly breeds in Middle and Upper River, but no nest yet found. Mostly recorded from Sapu and Georgetown area where present throughout the year, 1974–77 (M. E. J. Gore); Kudang, 21 Feb 1989 (T. Wacher). Only records from Lower River are singles at Yundum, 8 and 25 May, Camaloo, 15 and 22 May 1966 (Bray *et al.*) and Tendaba, Nov 1984 (Ericsson 1989).

70. CIRCUS AERUGINOSUS PV, WV

Marsh Harrier

Previously considered to be a not uncommon Palaearctic passage and winter visitor (*C.a. aeruginosus*) to freshwater marshes throughout the country. Recorded Sep–Apr, most arriving Oct; also 2 records in Jun and one in Aug (Bray *et al.*). However, has become less common in recent years, probably due to excessive shooting during migration in the Mediterranean and North Africa.

71. CIRCUS MACROURUS PV, WV

Pallid (or Pale) Harrier

Scarce Palaearctic passage and winter visitor, probably more numerous than *C. pygargus*, but see that species. Described as fairly numerous up-country on fallow escarpments and along the borders of bush, Feb–Mar (GOS Rev).

72. CIRCUS PYGARGUS WV

Montagu's Harrier

Rare Palaearctic winter visitor in open country; all records are from Lower and Middle River, Jan–Mar, except one, a male near Basse, 31 Dec 1980 (GOS ABR 1980). (It is not possible to separate females and immatures from *C. macrourus* and the many records of 'ring-tail' harriers could refer to either species.)

73. POLYBOROIDES RADIATUS (=GYMNOGENYS TYPICUS) RB

Harrier-hawk (or Gymnogene)

Resident and common in open agricultural land and open bush with scattered trees throughout the country. Numbers appear to have increased since 1980. Breeds Feb–Jun.

74. TERATHOPIUS ECAUDATUS RB*

Bateleur

Formerly resident and not uncommon in open forest and open country with scattered trees inland from about Mile 50. Today it is scarce and regularly reported only from Kiang West; there are recent records from Mansakonko inland to Pakali Ba; occasionally seen east to Basse. Once at Yundum but no records from the coast. Breeding probably occurs (juveniles have been seen) but there is no record of a nest.

Accipitrini

75. ACCIPITER BADIUS RB

Shikra

Common resident (*A.b. sphenurus*) in open forest and woodland throughout the country; regularly occurs in the larger gardens at Fajara and breeds annually in the dry season at the Medical Research Council Laboratories; C/2 in Apr (Cawkell & Moreau); courtship observed in Mar (Bray *et al.*).

76. ACCIPITER ERYTHROPUS (=MINULLUS) RB

West African Little Sparrowhawk

Rare resident (*A.e. minullus*) in open woodland, recorded only in Lower and Middle River. There are several recent records from Abuko Nature Reserve and singles at Pirang, Oct 1986 (GGFP) and at Marakissa, Jan 1989 (C. R. Barlow). Walton reported that it bred in May (Cawkell & Moreau).

77. ACCIPITER MELANOLEUCUS AV

Great (or Black) Sparrowhawk

African vagrant, one record only: a single at Tanji, 28 Apr 1963 (Cawkell 1965).

78. ACCIPITER NISUS AV

Sparrowhawk

Rare vagrant, 2 records only: single females near Diabugu, 20 Feb 1974 and at Buiba 21 Feb 1976 (Jensen & Kirkeby 1980). An uncommon Palaearctic visitor to West Africa.

79. ACCIPITER TOUSSENELII (=MACROCELIDES, =TACHIRO) RB*

West African Goshawk

Scarce resident (presumably *A.t. macrocelides*) in forest. Recorded throughout the year and almost certainly breeds (probably regularly) in thick woodland within Abuko Nature Reserve, Dec–Mar, but no nest has ever been found.

80. MELIERAX (=MICRONISUS) GABAR — RB?

Gabar Goshawk

Hopkinson described it as fairly common (Bannerman 1930–51), but it is now scarce. Probably resident, though no nest has been located.

81. MELIERAX METABATES — RB

Chanting Goshawk

Resident (*M.m. metabates*), not uncommon and widely distributed in open scrub and agricultural land with scattered trees throughout the country. Breeds Feb, C/3, (Cawkell & Moreau) to Jul (GOS ABR 1980).

Buteini

82. BUTASTUR RUFIPENNIS — DSV, (?RB)

Grasshopper Buzzard

Intra-African migrant. A not uncommon non-breeding dry season visitor in open country, arriving late Oct–early Nov and present until Feb; often seen at bush fires. More common inland, only occasionally seen near the coast. A pair was present at Yundum, Aug–Sep 1989 and courtship was observed so may occasionally breed (C. R. Barlow).

83. BUTEO AUGURALIS — (DSV)

Red-tailed (or Red-necked) Buzzard

Probably an irregular dry season visitor but there are only five positive sightings, all singles: Banjul, 4 Jul 1965 (Bray *et al.*); Missira (not located), 31 Mar 1975; Tendaba, 2 Nov 1977 (Jensen & Kirkeby 1980); Kiang West, 25 Dec 1985 (GOS RR); Basse, 11 Feb 1987 (GOS ABR 1986–87). There are a number of other recent records (all for Dec) but insufficient details have been supplied for them to be accepted.

84. BUTEO BUTEO — AV

Steppe Buzzard

Vagrant from the Palaearctic: one accepted record (presumably *B.b. vulpinus*) only: a single bird in company with *Milvus migrans* and one *Hieraaetus pennatus* near Tendaba, Dec 1973 (GOS Rev).

85. BUTEO RUFINUS — AV

Long-legged Buzzard

Vagrant from the Palaearctic, one accepted record only: a single bird (photographed) at Soma, 18 Dec 1973 (Jensen & Kirkeby 1980). An uncommon winter visitor to West Africa, recorded in Senegal.

86. KAUPIFALCO MONOGRAMMICUS RB

Lizard Buzzard

Common resident, widely distributed in open woodland and on the borders of forest and open country with scattered trees. Only breeding record is May, C/3 (Cawkell & Moreau); carrying nesting material at Sapu, Nov 1985 (M. E. J. Gore).

Aquilini

87. AQUILA RAPAX RB

Tawny Eagle

Rare resident (*A.r. belisarius*) in open country with scattered trees, mostly in Lower and Middle River. Breeding season Jan–Apr; nest C/2 in baobab tree, 9 Jan 1929 (Bannerman 1930–51).

88. AQUILA WAHLBERGI RB

Wahlberg's Eagle

Scarce resident, widely distributed in open bush with scattered tall trees and secondary forest, throughout the country. Only breeding record is nest with 2 half-grown young in tall tree near Bansang, 23 Feb 1975 (GOS ABR 1975).

89. HALIAETUS (=CUNCUMA) VOCIFER RB

West African River Eagle (or African Fish Eagle)

Common resident along Middle and Upper River; scarce in Lower River and only occasionally on the coast. Breeds Oct–Mar.

[HIERAAETUS DUBIUS (=AYRESI)

Ayre's Hawk-eagle

One possible record: a single bird photographed near Elephant I., 13 Jan 1984. As the photograph was not sufficiently clear and the bird could have been an immature *Haliaetus vocifer* the record was not accepted (GOS RR).]

90. HIERAAETUS PENNATUS (WV)

Booted Eagle

Probably an irregular Palaearctic winter visitor, described as rare migrant to West Africa (Serle *et al.*) and previously considered as being only an accidental visitor to The Gambia. Recorded on 6 occasions in Lower and Middle River before 1980, Dec–Jan, and 6 subsequent times Dec–Feb, though in all cases post 1980 the observers failed to supply a detailed description. It is likely to occur in most years.

91. HEIRAAETUS SPILOGASTER (=FASCIATUS) RB

African Hawk-eagle

Rare resident, widely distributed in open forest throughout the country. Breeds Dec–Apr. Nest 25 m up in a *Daniellia oliveri* in the amenity belt at Kabafitta Forest Reserve was known to have been occupied for several years; C/2, 1 Feb 1978, one bird fledged mid-Apr (M. E. J. Gore).

92. LOPHAETUS OCCIPITALIS RB

Long-crested Hawk-eagle

Resident and not uncommon; widely distributed in open country, particularly favouring wetlands and may often be seen perched in the open on a stake or dead tree in freshwater marshes and ricefields. Only breeding record is Apr, C/2 (Cawkell & Moreau).

93. POLEMAETUS BELLICOSUS RB

Martial Eagle

Rare resident though there is no recent breeding record. One young bird was taken and sent to the London Zoo in 1910 (no date given) and Hopkinson saw it once on MacCarthy I. and 'two or three at other times' (Bannerman 1930–51). Recent records (all singles) are: Denton Bridge, 11 Feb; Banjul, 11 Feb; Yundum, 9 Sep 1962 (Cawkell & Moreau), 21 Oct 1964, on several occasions between Apr and Jun 1966 (Bray *et al.*); Fulabantang, 15 Feb 1963; Lamin, a male seen frequently, May–Jul 1963 (Cawkell 1965); Middle River 10 Jan 1966; Banjul Bund, 15 May 1965; Jakhaly, 8 Dec 1977 (GOS ABR 1977); Kiang West regularly in 1985–86; Basse, Dec 1984; Wallikunda, Jan 1986 (GOS RR); Brikama, May 1986 (C. R. Barlow).

[STEPHANOAETUS CORONATUS Rejected

Crowned Hawk-eagle (or Eagle)

According to the observers, the 1973 record included in brackets in Jensen & Kirkeby (1980) is very doubtful; it should be discounted.]

Milvini

94. AVICEDA CUCULOIDES AV

West African Cuckoo Falcon

African vagrant. Bannerman (1930–51) states that it is possibly a visitor in the rains, presumably on evidence from Hopkinson, but the only records (all singles) since have been mainly in the dry season: Brikama, Jun 1956; Karantaba, 22 Jan 1960 (Cawkell 1965), 2 Dec 1974 (Jensen & Kirkeby 1980); Kabafitta, 2 Feb 1979 (GOS ABR 1979); Brikama, 1 Jun 1980 (GOS ABR 1980); Abuko, 19 and 26 Feb 1984 (GOS RR); Tanji, Nov 1986; Marakissa, May 1989 (C. R. Barlow).

95. ELANUS CAERULEUS DSV, (RB)

Black-shouldered Kite

Erratic dry season visitor (*E.c. caeruleus*), in some years (most recently 1987–88) common, in others scarce. Most presumably move north to breed during the rains, Jul–Oct, but recorded in all months and a few pairs may nest most years, though the only record (undated) is of 3 young in a nest taken by Hopkinson (Bannerman 1930–51).

96. ELANUS (=CHELICTINIA) RIOCOURII DSV

Swallow-tailed Kite

Rare intra-African migrant, occurring anywhere in open country in Middle and Upper River after the rains, Dec–Apr; one record for May. Very occasionally reported near the coast: singles Yundum, Apr 1978 (M. E. J. Gore); Cape St Mary, Dec 1986; Camaloo, Dec 1987 (W. E. Waters).

97. MACHEIRHAMPHUS ALCINUS ?

Bat Hawk (or Bat-eating Buzzard)

Status uncertain, only 4 records (all singles): Kaur, 3 Nov 1956, 4 Apr 1958 (on both occasions the birds were preying on bats streaming out of the resthouse roof at dusk (Cawkell & Moreau)); Fajara on several days in Jan 1963 (I. A. McGregor); Tendaba, 24 Nov 1982 (GOS RR). Serle *et al.* (1977) describe it as widely but thinly distributed from The Gambia south to Congo.

98. MILVUS MIGRANS WV, DSV, MB

Black Kite

It is not always possible in the field to separate the Palaearctic migrant (*M.m. migrans*) from the African race (*M.m. parasitus*), which is an intra-African migrant, but both occur, the latter being the more numerous. Common on the coast Oct–Apr. Present inland until Jul. Nesting recorded Apr and May, but breeding numbers are small (GOS Rev).

99. MILVUS MILVUS AV

Red Kite

Vagrant from the Palaearctic, two excellent sightings: one over the pools of Abuko Nature Reserve on 17 Dec 1987; another, probably the same individual, near the village of Jambur (Jambuorr), 10 km south of Abuko, on 25 Dec 1987. The only other records from sub-Saharan Africa are from South Africa and Kenya (Geeson & Geeson 1990).

100. PERNIS APIVORUS (PV), (WV)

Honey Buzzard

Occasional passage and winter visitor from the Palaearctic, few records (all singles): Mansakonko, 9 Apr 1966 (Bray *et al.*); Basse, 29 Dec (no year given) (GOS Rev); by roadside in Lower River, late Feb 1973 (J. N. Dymond & M. Wright); Banjul, 5 Jan 1975 and Mandinari, 19 Jan 1975 (GOS ABR 1975); Soma, 20 Jan; Jibora, 1 Jun (an unusual date) and Tendaba, early Nov 1977 (GOS ABR 1977); Fajara, 14 Feb 1981 (GOS ABR 1981); Abuko, 1 Apr 1983 (GOS RR). Probably largely overlooked.

SAGITTARIIDAE

101. SAGITTARIUS SERPENTARIUS AV

Secretary-bird

Formerly described as not uncommon in Upper River in open country during the rains, Jul-Oct (Bannerman 1930–51). The only records since are of 3 single birds at Sapu between 1957 and 1962 (no dates given) (Cawkell & Moreau). [Jensen & Kirkeby (1980) record a juvenile at Abuko, 21 Jan 1973, drinking at the main pool, but in view of the habitat this seems doubtful.]

FALCONIDAE

102. FALCO ALOPEX AV

Fox Kestrel

African vagrant, 3 records only (all singles): Kaur, 19 May 1957 (Cawkell 1965); at Tanji (in a swarm of locusts), 29 Oct 1986 (C. R. Barlow, N. Hall); in Upper River, Oct 1988 (R. Webzell *et al.*). A record of one at Tendaba, 19 Dec 1983 was not accepted as no details were supplied (GOS RR).

103. FALCO ARDOSIACEUS RB

Grey Kestrel

Common and widespread resident in open country. Often nests in the top of dead oil palm trees; one in an old Hammerkop's nest at Yoroberikunda in Apr (Bray *et al.*).

104. FALCO BIARMICUS AfM

Lanner Falcon

Scarce but regular intra-African migrant. Confirmed sightings: Banjul, one on 3 Nov 1965 (Bray *et al.*); Lower River, one in late Feb 1973 (J. N. Dymond & M. Wright); near Basse, one late Feb 1973 and 2 on 14 Dec; Yundum, 2 on 21 Dec 1975 (GOS ABR 1975) and one on 9 May 1976 (GOS ABR 1976); Keneba, one on 15 Jan; Somita, one on 17 Apr; Bwiam, one on 1 Jul 1977; Camaloo, one on 8 Sep (GOS ABR 1977); Kotu, one on 15 Dec 1979 (R. Hume, D. Fisher). There have been 10 records since 1982 (all Nov–Jan) except one at Kiang West, 23 Jun 1985 (GOS RR).

105. FALCO CHICQUERA RB

Red-necked Kestrel (or Falcon)

Scarce resident (*F.c. ruficollis*), normally associated with the rhun palm *Borassus aethiopium*. Individuals and pairs recorded in most months: 4 in rhun palm plantation near Sapu, 14 Apr 1975 (GOS ABR 1975); 2 at Bushfire at Tendaba, 10 Feb 1987 (GOS ABR 1987). Pair behaving as if establishing territory at Fajara, Dec–Jan 1977/8; breeding confirmed in 1979 — 3 nestlings in nest in rhun palm, Jun (GOS ABR 1979).

106. FALCO CUVIERI RB*

African Hobby

Scarce, probably resident, in open forest. Most records are from Lower River but has been recorded east to Basse. Reported in all months and almost certainly breeds but there is no evidence.

107. FALCO NAUMANNI (WV)

Lesser Kestrel

Rare and irregular Palaearctic winter visitor in open country but may well be overlooked. Most records from near the coast: 4 in Jan 1972 (GOS Rev); Abuko, one on 10 Jan; Camaloo, one on 19 Feb 1975 (GOS ABR 1975); Banjul, 6 on 11 Feb 1978 (M. E. J. Gore); one on 16 and 19 Jan 1983 (GOS RR); Kaur, one on 25 Mar 1981 (GOS ABR 1981).

108. FALCO PEREGRINUS (PV), (WV)

Peregrine Falcon

Rare and irregular visitor: 10 records Aug–May (Bray *et al.*, GOS Rev, GOS RR) probably all refer to the nominate, European race *F.p. peregrinus*, which is a rare winter visitor to West Africa. Singles at Abuko as late as 24 Jun 1962 and 25 Jul 1963 (Cawkell 1965) and Basse, 13 Jul 1980 (GOS ABR 1980) probably belong to the African race *F.p. minor*, which has a wide but local distribution in open and mountainous country south of the Sahara to South Africa. There is an undated specimen of this race taken in The Gambia (Bannerman 1930–51). It is unlikely to breed, as suitable nesting sites are not available.

109. FALCO SUBBUTEO PV, (WV)

Hobby

Regular but scarce passage visitor from the Palaearctic, mainly Nov and Apr, with 3–4 reported most years. Has been recorded between 26 Aug and 21 May, including Dec–Feb, so the occasional bird may well over-winter.

110. FALCO TINNUNCULUS WV

Kestrel

Palaearctic winter visitor (*F.t. tinnunculus*), not uncommon in open country. The majority are females or immatures. Most numerous Dec–Mar, but has been recorded between 8 Oct and 15 May.

PHASIANIDAE
Phasianinae — Perdicini

111. COTURNIX COTURNIX (WV)

Common Quail

Rare and irregular Palaearctic winter visitor (*C.c. coturnix*) in open country, apparently less numerous than previously for Hopkinson described it as by no means uncommon from mid-Nov to Feb or Mar (Bannerman 1930–51). The only recent records are Camaloo, one in winter 1973–74 (no date given) (GOS Rev); Cape St Mary, one on 17 Jan 1983; Kotu, one on 14 Jan 1984; Basse, 4 on 26 Jan 1984, 2 on 22 Dec 1984 (GOS RR); Kiang West, one on 25 Nov 1986 (J. N. Dymond).

112. FRANCOLINUS AHANTENSIS RB?

Ahanta Francolin

Rare and very local (*F.a. hopkinsoni*), probably resident in remaining thick forest, but breeding has never been proved. Hopkinson knew of only 7 shot during his 28 years in The Gambia (Bannerman 1930–51). The only records since are: Abuko Nature Reserve, Apr 1974 (GOS Rev), Dec 1977 (GOS ABR 1977), and a probable in Dec 1986 (GOS ABR 1986–87); Pirang, singles seen on a total of 8 days in May 1985 and Oct 1986 (G.G.F.P.). The race *F.a. hopkinsoni* (admitted by White) is confined to The Gambia and Guinea Bissau.

113. FRANCOLINUS ALBOGULARIS ?

White-throated Francolin

Hopkinson described it as rare but locally distributed (*F.a. albogularis*) throughout the country, preferring thicker cover than *F. bicalcaratus* (Bannerman 1930–51). There is only one recent record: a single bird at Tendaba, 24 Nov 1984 (GOS RR).

114. FRANCOLINUS BICALCARATUS RB

Double-spurred Francolin

The main game-bird (*F.b. bicalcaratus*); common throughout the country, spending most of the day on the ground in dense woodland and forest and coming out into the groundnut fields and other open cultivated areas to feed in the early morning and late afternoon. Mostly roosts in trees in forest. Breeding season is extended. Courtship has been noted in Aug and chicks and flying young seen Nov–Apr, most Mar–Apr.

115. PTILOPACHUS PETROSUS RB

Stone-partridge

Locally common (*P.p. petrosus*), usually on dry laterite outcrops, but occurs also in open woodland. Most numerous in Middle and Upper River, but small numbers occur in suitable country to the coast, e.g. at Brufut and Tanji. Breeding recorded May–Jul; probably also earlier as many had small young in Niokola-Koba National Park, Senegal, 120 km east of Basse in early Apr 1975 (M. E. J. Gore).

Numidinae

116. NUMIDA MELEAGRIS RB

Grey-breasted Helmet (or Helmetted) Guinea-fowl

Today a scarce local resident (*N.m. galeata*) in riverine forest, though flocks may sometimes be encountered in open bush. Numbers have decreased, almost certainly as a result of hunting; during the 1970s it was not uncommon with flocks of 20–50 regularly reported from Brikama, Keneba, Karantaba, Baboon I. and Jakhaly but only small numbers have been reported since 1980.

TURNICIDAE

[ORTYXELOS MEIFFRENII Rejected

Quail Plover

Having examined skins and watched a pair of *Turnix sylvatica* at close range, I have no doubt that the birds described as Quail Plovers *Ortyxelos meiffrenii* and as breeding at Brufut, Mar–Apr 1975 (GOS ABR 1975) and also seen 5 km away in Feb 1976 (GOS ABR 1976), were in fact *T. sylvatica*. A record of one at Cape St Mary, 3 Dec 1986 was also not accepted (GOS RR).]

117. TURNIX SYLVATICA RB

African Button-Quail

Probably a widely distributed resident (*T.s. lepurana*) in open grassland, but rarely seen. Recorded Brikama, Cape St Mary and Brufut, where a chick was seen in 1975 and a pair May–June 1977 (GOS ABR 1977).

GRUIDAE

118. BALEARICA PAVONINA RB

Crowned Crane

Uncommon resident (*B.p. pavonina*), most numerous in Middle River; flocks of up to 50 on suitable open ground by the river during the dry season; maximum 110 at Jakhaly, early Jul 1976 (GOS ABR 1976). Small parties often present near Brumen Bridge. Few records nearer the coast: Banjul Bund, 2 between Dec–Jan 1965–66 (Bray *et al.*); Mandinari, 4 on 5 Mar 1976 (GOS ABR 1976); Pirang, *c.* 40 in May 1986 (G.G.F.P.), 16 on 25 Nov 1986 (J. N. Dymond). Bannerman (1930–51) reported breeding in some areas. especially Niamina and Morel (1972) reported breeding Sep–Oct. Undoubtedly breeds today, but only recent evidence is pair with juvenile among party at Pirang, Nov 1986.

RALLIDAE
Rallinae

119. CREX (=CRECOPSIS) EGREGIA RB*

African Crake

Scarce resident in freshwater swamps throughout the country, but rarely seen as it usually remains in cover. Records for all months from Banjul Bund, Camaloo, Abuko, Jakhaly and Basse. Certainly breeds but no nest has ever been found.

120. GALLINULA ANGULATA ?RB

Lesser Moorhen

Until 1979, only 3 records, all singles: Basse, 29 Aug 1956 (Cawkell & Moreau); Kolior, 4 Jul 1971 (Jensen & Kirkeby 1980); Jakhaly, 8 Apr 1978 (J. Bryan & P. Manser). Since 1979 the records are: Mile 129, one on 23 Jan and one on 15 Aug 1979; Bansang, 3 on 18 Aug (A. Moore, P. Goll), one on 16 Sep 1980 (GOS ABR 1980); Abuko Nature Reserve, one on 28 Feb; Camaloo, one on 22 Sep 1981 (GOS ABR 1981). Several records from the Senegal River delta, including a bird collected in breeding condition, Aug 1963 (Morel 1972), are in the expected breeding season. Occurrence and breeding in The Gambia probably overlooked.

121. GALLINULA CHLOROPUS ?RB, WV, AfM

Moorhen

The African race, *G.c. brachyptera*, cannot be separated in the field from the nominate European race; Gambian birds may therefore be local residents, intra-African migrants or migrants from Europe (*G.c. chloropus*). Uncommon in freshwater marshes. Most records fall between Nov and Apr, suggesting immigration. In 'summer' only reported near Basse, 26 Jul and 10 Aug 1959 (Cawkell & Moreau) and on riverbank at Sapu, 29 May 1974 (GOS Rev). Recent 'wintering' records are: Darsilami, one in Apr 1973 (GOS Rev); Sapu, one in Mar 1975 (GOS ABR 1975); Camaloo, 2–3 from Feb–Mar 1976 and also from Dec 1976–Apr 1977 (GOS ABR 1976–77); Jakhaly, 10, mostly immatures, on 14 Jan 1978 (M. E. J. Gore), one on 8 Apr 1978 (J. Bryan & P. Evans) and 13 Apr (P. Manser); Abuko, 4 on 19 Feb 1978 (P. Evans). There were 3 records in 1979 (GOS ABR 1979) and 10 more, all during the dry season, 1982–86 (GOS RR).

122. LIMNOCORAX FLAVIROSTRA RB

Black Crake

Resident and common in swamps (however insignificant) from the coast to the extreme eastern part of the country; also found along the river edge above Kaur, where the water is always fresh. Breeding season is extended and possibly nests most months when swamp conditions are suitable. Recorded breeding Jun and Sep in Upper River (Cawkell & Moreau); chicks seen at Camaloo in Dec and at Yundum in Jan (Bray *et al.*).

123. PORZANA PORZANA AV

Spotted Crake

Rare Palaearctic vagrant. The only acceptable record is one heard calling in dense grass at Pirang, Oct 1988 (G.G.F.P.), the researchers being familiar with the call. One reported off Banjul Bund, 24 Apr 1982 was considered probable as it occurs in Nigeria (Elgood 1982) and Ivory Coast (Thiollay 1985) but insufficient details were supplied by the observers for it to be accepted (GOS RR).

124. PORPHYRIO (=PORPHYRULA) ALLENI ?RB

Allen's Reed-hen (or Gallinule)

Status uncertain; probably a rare resident in overgrown swamps and ricefields, but easily overlooked. Until 1988 records, all singles, were from Middle and Upper River: Basse, Aug 1963, Jan 1966; Sapu, 9 Oct 1972, 21 Oct 1974 (GOS Rev) and 6 Apr 1978 (N. & J. Eyre). A single bird at Abuko Nature Reserve, Jan 1988 (C. White) and 20 Nov 1988 (J. N. Dymond) and a sub-adult at Marakissa, Jan–Feb 1989 (C. R. Barlow) are the first records from Lower River.

125. PORPHYRIO PORPHYRIO (=MADAGASCARIENSIS) (DSV)

King Reed-hen (or Purple Gallinule)

A rare and irregular dry season visitor (*P.p. madagascariensis*) in reed-covered marshes: Kaur, 6 together in Jun 1972, one in Jul 1973 (GOS Rev); Camaloo, 2 in Jan–May 1977 with one remaining until early Sep and 2 there Apr–May 1989 (C. R. Barlow *et al.*); Middle River, 2 on 4 Dec 1977 (GOS ABR 1977); Jakhaly, one on 15 Jan 1978 (M. E. J. Gore). Breeding reported in Nov, at the end of the rains, north of Dakar in Senegal (Morel 1972) but elsewhere in West Africa breeds during the rains e.g. Jul–Aug at Sokoto, Nigeria (Elgood 1982). It appears therefore to be a non-breeding visitor to The Gambia.

126. SAROTHRURA PULCHRA RB?

White-spotted Pigmy Rail (or White-spotted Crake)

Status uncertain. One of the most difficult birds to observe. Probably a rare resident (*S.p. pulchra*) in riverine forest and overgrown swampland, but very few records. Bannerman (1930–51) refers to 3 specimens from 'Gambia and Portuguese Guinea'. Recorded at Pakalinding, Nov 1947 (Bray *et al.*). All records since are of individuals seen on numerous occasions, 1972–88 at Abuko Nature Reserve.

HELIORNITHIDAE

127. PODICA SENEGALENSIS RB*

Finfoot

Resident (*P.s. senegalensis*) and probably not uncommon along the River Gambia and tributaries, but only rarely seen. Records in all months from Abuko Nature Reserve, Lamin, Brikama, Mandinari, Tendaba, Ndemban, Elephant I., Georgetown, Bansang and Basse, and on the coast at Kotu Stream. Breeding probable (but not recorded) since it is considered sedentary.

OTIDIDAE

128. EUPODOTIS (=LISSOTIS) MELANOGASTER RB

Black-bellied Bustard

Scarce resident; numbers have decreased since 1980. Previously not uncommon and regularly reported 1961–77 at Yundum (where it undoubtedly bred near the airport) with other records from Brikama, Bwiam, Keneba, Jakhaly and Basse. Very few recent records. Breeding recorded in Aug (Bray *et al.*).

129. EUPODOTIS SENEGALENSIS AV, FB

Senegal Bustard

Described by Hopkinson as the commonest bustard (*E.s. senegalensis*) resident in The Gambia (Bannerman 1930–51), being widespread in open country. In the early 1960s was still considered more numerous than *E. melanogaster*, but uncommon (Cawkell & Moreau). Today it is a rare visitor; there are only 3 recent records: Kiang West, a female, almost certainly the same bird, on 15 and 31 May 1986 (GOS RR); Bijilo, one on 12 Apr 1988 (GOS group); Pakali Ba, one on 10 May 1989 (D. Clifford). Walton reported breeding in Feb (Cawkell & Moreau).

130. NEOTIS DENHAMI AV

Denham's Bustard

Hopkinson (Bannerman 1930–51) reported that it was not uncommon spasmodically in open country in winter (*N.d. denhami*), but now dangerously overhunted over much of its range across Africa. Since Hopkinson's day, the only records (all singles) are: Sapu, a female on 17 Sep 1979 (C. V. Eyre); Somita, one on 15 Dec 1973; near Albreda, one on 25 Dec 1975 (Jensen & Kirkeby 1980). Probable sightings near Banjul, 10 Jul 1965, on sand-dunes near Fajara, 28 Jun 1966 (Bray *et al.*), near Bwiam (GOS ABR 1977), and in Middle River in Dec 1983 (GOS RR).

131. OTIS (=ARDEOTIS) ARABS AV

Sudan (or Arabian) Bustard

Never more than a rare visitor (*O.a. stieberi*) in eastern Gambia. Last record, one near Bakendik collected by Lowe in Dec 1928 (Bannerman 1930–51).

JACANIDAE

132. ACTOPHILORNIS AFRICANA RB

Lily-trotter (or African Jacana)

Resident and common in freshwater swamps throughout the country. Numbers concentrate in the few areas which retain water during the dry season. Breeds Jun–Dec, occasionally later; most eggs hatch early Nov when the rains are ending. Two chicks about 2 weeks old near Brufut, 14 Mar 1976 (GOS ABR 1976).

ROSTRATULIDAE

133. ROSTRATULA BENGHALENSIS AfM, MB?

Painted Snipe

Scarce, mainly dry season visitor, but recorded in most months (*R.b. benghalensis*). Lowe collected one, 27 Dec 1929, which he described as 'laying' (Bannerman 1930–51). No nest has ever been found and it is doubtful that it breeds in The Gambia. Up to 100 (4–5 males to one female) were present at one pool at Jakhaly, Feb 1975, *c.* 50 were at another pool (GOS ABR 1975) and up to 20 appear most years, Mar–May at Camaloo, which indicates concentration at the few freshwater swamps which retain water late in the dry season. Other recent records are: Basse, Jun; Georgetown, Aug; Banjul Bund, Oct–Nov; Cape St Mary, Dec; Jakhaly, Aug and Nov.

HAEMATOPODIDAE

134. HAEMATOPUS OSTRALEGUS PV, WV

Oyster-catcher

Palaearctic migrant (*H.o. ostralegus*) common on passage along the coast; a few over-winter. First arrivals late Jul; numbers increase, with flocks of up to 40 passing Oct–Nov. Smaller numbers occur Mar–Apr. Occasionally non-breeding birds over-summer.

RECURVIROSTRIDAE

135. HIMANTOPUS HIMANTOPUS PV, WV

Black-winged Stilt

Most common Sep–Nov and Feb–Apr; parties up to 10, occasionally more, on freshwater marshes throughout the country. These are probably mostly Palaearctic migrants from north African and southern European breeding grounds (a Dutch-ringed bird was observed at Kotu sewage farm, Dec 1987). No evidence of breeding or intra-African migration but recorded in every month of the year so some records may represent the African population.

136. RECURVIROSTRA AVOSETTA PV, WV

Avocet

Uncommon visitor from the Palaearctic; previously mostly singles or 2–3 were reported near the coast, Feb–Apr, occasionally Sep–Dec. Flock of 10 off Bund Road, 22 Dec with 6 there 26 Dec 1981 (GOS ABR 1981). Until 1979 only one large flock had been recorded: 56 flying downstream opposite Tendaba, 8 Mar 1976 (GOS ABR 1976). Since 1984 flocks of about 40 (maximum 60 at Yellitenda, 25 Jan 1989 (G. Rainey)) regularly occur on mudflats in Lower and Middle River, Dec–Feb. Over 700 were seen on salt flats at Kaolack in Senegal, Dec–Jan 1964–65 by G. & P. Gore (*Ibis* 108: 281), who suggested that there might be undiscovered wintering grounds among the large areas of undisturbed mangrove in Lower River in The Gambia also.

BURHINIDAE

137. BURHINUS (=OEDICNEMUS) CAPENSIS ?

Spotted Thick-knee

Status uncertain, 4 records only: Lowe collected one in 1929; Bwiam, a pair on extensive dry saltpan behaving as if nesting, 7–8 Jun 1956 (E. M. Cawkell); near Wallikunda, one seen at close range at dusk in dry, open bush, 8 Feb 1975 (GOS Rev); near Brumen Bridge, one on 8 Feb 1987 (GOS ABR 1986–87).

138. BURHINUS (=OEDICNEMUS) SENEGALENSIS RB

Senegal Thick-knee

Common and widespread near water; flocks of up to 30 in mangrove and along the river banks during and after the rains, Dec–Mar. Breeding season is evidently extended, e.g. Walton reported nesting Apr–May (Cawkell & Moreau) and C/2 found Jakhaly, 25 Oct 1974 (GOS Rev).

[BURHINUS (=OEDICNEMUS) VERMICULATUS Rejected

Water Thick-knee

One (unconfirmed) record (GOS Rev): a single seen by Mr John Conway on the river bank at Georgetown, end Mar (no year given), is not considered acceptable.]

GLAREOLIDAE
Cursoriinae

139. CURSORIUS (=RHINOPTILUS) CHALCOPTERUS RB?

Bronze-wing (or Violet-tipped) Courser

Rare resident, possibly subject to local migration. Recorded in most months and probably breeds, but no nest found. Typical records: Jakhaly, one on 25 Feb, 2–3 on 10 Apr 1975; between Brumen Bridge and Soma, 10 along road at dawn, 22 Dec 1975 (GOS ABR 1975); Brufut, 1–4 on several occasions, 26 Jun–6 Jul 1977 (GOS ABR 1977); Yundum, 2 on 24 Jan 1978 (M. E. Smalley). Between 1982–86 singles or pairs were recorded in Lower River on 7 occasions (GOS RR); a pair behaving as if they were nesting in open woodland behind Jakhaly swamp, 19 Mar 1977 (GOS ABR 1977).

140. CURSORIUS CURSOR AV

Cream-coloured Courser

African vagrant, 2 records only: one (not 5 as stated in GOS ABR 1978) observed on the sand at Mile 5, 4 Dec 1966 (Bray *et al.* Addenda 1967); 2 near Yundum, 22 Jan 1971 (Morel 1972).

141. CURSORIUS TEMMINICKII RB

Temminck's Courser

Uncommon resident in suitable open country; locally common around Yundum airport where 30–40 were present in pairs and small parties, Jan–Feb 1976; also reported from Cape Road, Sukuta, Keneba and Koina. Pair feeding 2 newly-hatched chicks at Yundum, 3 Feb 1976 (GOS ABR 1976).

142. PLUVIANUS AEGYPTIUS DSV

Crocodile Bird (or Egyptian Plover)

Parties of 5–8 (once 15) occur along Upper River, regularly at Basse; occasionally in Middle River west to Farafenni, mainly during the dry season Nov–Apr, but recorded in most months. Recorded at Sapu, 21 Jun 1974 (GOS Rev) and 15 Jul 1977 (GOS ABR 1977); at Farafenni, 7 on 29 Oct 1974 (GOS Rev); near Soma, one on 30 Aug 1975 (GOS ABR 1975). One to two seen annually on north bank between Kaur and Kudang, Nov–Dec 1982–89 (G. Rainey). Breeds along the upper reaches of the Gambia River in Senegal but there is no evidence that it has ever done so in The Gambia.

Glareolinae

[GLAREOLA NORDMANNI

Black-winged Pratincole

Bannerman (1930–51) reported that Hopkinson 'is nearly certain that he has seen these pratincoles with black axillaries, but has not shot specimens'. No other references.]

143. GLAREOLA PRATINCOLA WV, RB?

Pratincole

Mainly a not uncommon Palaearctic visitor (*G.p. pratincola*) with probably a small resident population (*G.p. fulleborni*). Most numerous in Middle River; up to 40 reported in flocks near Farafenni in Oct and at Jakhaly, Feb–May. Smaller numbers recorded in Lower and Upper River. Breeding suspected at Pakali Ba, Jun 1956 (Cawkell & Moreau).

CHARADRIIDAE

144. CHARADRIUS (=LEUCOPOLIUS) ALEXANDRINUS PV, WV

Kentish Plover

Scarce Palaearctic winter visitor (*C.a. alexandrinus*) on the coast, usually in small flocks up to 20; most numerous Dec–Feb, but recorded 20 Aug–6 May. No records inland.

145. CHARADRIUS DUBIUS PV, WV

Little Ringed Plover

Scarce passage and winter visitor from the Palaearctic (*C.d. curonicus*) Aug–May, most numerous on passage Nov and Mar. Occurs mainly inland by the river and freshwater marshes: flocks up to 20 at Jakhaly; *c.* 40 on playing field at

Yundum, 27 Dec 1973, remained in reducing numbers until 22 Mar 1974, when 5 still present (GOS Rev); *c*. 50 Keneba, 20 Nov 1977 (GOS ABR 1977). On coast usually only singles or up to 5 together, but 15 at Barra, 9 Dec 1981 (GOS ABR 1981).

146. CHARADRIUS FORBESI — AV

Forbes's Banded Plover

African vagrant, only one record: one by a laterite pool near Bansang, 23 Nov 1979 (GOS ABR 1979). A savanna species widely distributed inland in West Africa and subject to local movements.

147. CHARADRIUS HIATICULA — PV, WV

Ringed Plover

Common Palaearctic passage and winter visitor on the coast Aug–Apr; most numerous on passage Sep–Oct and Mar. Parties of 10–20 occur, mostly on passage, on inland swamps. Some non-breeding birds usually over-summer and has been recorded in every month.

148. CHARADRIUS (=LEUCOPOLIUS) MARGINATUS — RB

White-fronted Sand-plover

In the 1970s considered a scarce resident (*C.m. hesperius*) along the coast on suitable sand-dunes. First recorded at Mile 5, May 1962 (Cawkell & Moreau); young seen there Jul 1965 and Jul 1966 (Bray *et al.*). Pair with chick at Cape Lagoon, 15 May 1975 (GOS ABR 1975); a nest C/3, on sand-spit near Tanji, 23 and 30 May 1976, was empty 6 Jun (GOS ABR 1976). The species appears to have disappeared from the mainland as there have been no breeding records since. However, adults and young have been observed (C. R. Barlow) on the Bijilo Is. which reappeared in the early 1980s and it may be that the small resident population has moved there, possibly having originally come from the islands when they were inundated in the 1950s. Two at Cape St Mary, 14 Nov 1984 appears to be the most recent record on the mainland (Ericsson 1989).

149. CHARADRIUS (=LEUCOPOLIUS) PECUARIUS — DSV

Kittlitz's Sand Plover

Intra-African migrant; since 1965 up to 6 recorded (*C.p. pecuarius*) in most years, Dec–Jan, along Banjul Bund; in 1966, 5 remained until 29 Apr. Singles at Camaloo, 5 Nov and 20 Dec 1975. Records from up-river: 3 at Kaiaff and *c*. 40 beside lake at Fatoto, early Feb 1974 (GOS Rev). Known to breed near Richard-Toll in northern Senegal, Feb–Jul (Morel 1972), but no indication of breeding in The Gambia.

150. EUDROMIAS MORINELLUS — AV

Dotterel

Vagrant from the Palaearctic, one record only: a single bird (photographed) at Cape St Mary, 14 Mar 1985 (GOS RR).

151. PLUVIALIS APRICARIUS AV

(Eurasian) Golden Plover

There have been 6 records of Golden Plovers in The Gambia, 5 of which have been described as *P. apricarius*, a rare visitor from the Palaearctic, the other as *P. dominica* a rare Nearctic vagrant in West Africa (Serle *et al.* 1977). As the two are practically indistinguishable in winter only one of these records has been accepted as being definitely this species: a single bird near Wadner Beach Hotel, Banjul, 27 Dec 1981 (GOS ABR 1981). The other records of *P. apricarius*/*P. dominica* are: Fajara, 7 on Dec 1973 (GOS Rev); Cape St Mary, 2 on 17 Feb 1975; Banjul Bund, one on 29 Oct 1975 (GOS ABR 1975) and one in full breeding plumage near Cape St Mary, Apr–May 1986 (C. R. Barlow). A flock of *c.* 20 seen several times at Yundum Airport, Dec–Jan 1973–74 were probably *P. apricarius* but P. R. Colston (BMNH) is unable to be certain of this from a photograph taken of one of the birds.

152. PLUVIALIS DOMINICA AV

American Golden Plover

Nearctic vagrant, one record only: one at Fajara, 15 Jan 1984 (GOS RR); identified as this species from a photograph and field description (see notes under *P. apricarius* above).

153. PLUVIALIS (=SQUATAROLA) SQUATAROLA PV, WV

Grey Plover

Common Palaearctic passage and winter visitor on the coast; first arrivals Aug, most numerous on passage Sep–Oct and Mar when flocks of up to 30 occur. Wintering birds occur singly along the length of the coast. A few non-breeders usually over-summer.

154. VANELLUS (=XIPHIDIOPTERUS) ALBICEPS (DSV)

White-headed Plover

Rare and irregular dry season visitor to Upper River, occasionally Middle River, from the upper reaches of the Gambia River in Senegal where it is not uncommon. First recorded Jakhaly, one on 21 Jun 1974; Farafenni, one on 27 Oct 1974 (GOS Rev); Basse, 2 (photographed) on 27 Oct 1974 (GOS Rev), 2 on 3 Dec 1974 (Jensen & Kirkeby 1980), 5 on 29 Oct 1981 (GOS ABR 1981); Bansang, 2 on 5 Jan 1976 (GOS ABR 1976). There have been a number of recent records during the dry season at Basse and along the north bank of Upper River.

155. VANELLUS (=AFRIBYX) SENEGALLUS RB

Senegal Wattled Plover

Common resident (*V.s. senegallus*) throughout the country, most numerous in Lower River usually near water, but sometimes found in open bush. Breeds throughout the dry season; nests recorded Oct–Jul.

156. VANELLUS (=HOPLOPTERUS) SPINOSUS RB

Spur-winged Plover

Resident and common near freshwater marshes; occasionally on saline mud, but always in the vicinity of water. Breeding season is extended throughout the dry season, Dec–Jul, sometimes in the rains until Sep.

157. VANELLUS (=SARCIOPHORUS) TECTUS RB

Black-headed Plover

Widespread and common resident (*V.t. tectus*) in open country, agricultural land, sports fields, etc, and sometimes in clearings in secondary forest. Out of the breeding season occurs in parties of up to 30. Breeds Jan–Jul.

158. VANELLUS VANELLUS AV

Lapwing

Vagrant from the Palaearctic, 3 records all of which probably refer to the same bird: Cape St Mary area, 27 Nov 1986 and 11 and 31 Jan 1987 (GOS RR).

SCOLOPACIDAE
Tringinae

159. LIMOSA LAPPONICA PV, WV

Bar-tailed Godwit

Not uncommon Palaearctic passage and winter visitor (*L.l. lapponica*). Confined to the coast where total of up to 50 occur between Sep and Apr. A few non-breeding birds usually over-summer.

160. LIMOSA LIMOSA PV, WV

Black-tailed Godwit

Locally abundant Palaearctic passage and winter visitor (*L.l. limosa*) on rice swamps Jul–Apr. Flocks arrive Aug–Sep and numbers increase until Nov, when maximum of 800 recorded at Camaloo. A few non-breeding birds over-summer.

161. NUMENIUS ARQUATA PV, WV

Curlew

Uncommon Palaearctic passage and winter visitor (*N.a. arquata*) on the coast, occasionally inland to Middle River. *N.a. orientalis* also occurs, two birds of this race having been identified from flight photographs, and several observed, at Cape St Mary, 1–15 Jan 1988 (R. J. Chandler). (It has been suggested (Moreau 1972) that the majority of wintering Curlews south of Mauritania are this race.) Up to 12 on Cape Lagoon in winter; small numbers also occur along the creeks in the mangrove swamps near Banjul. An occasional non-breeding bird over-summers.

162. NUMENIUS PHAEOPUS PV, WV

Whimbrel

Common Palaearctic passage and winter visitor (*N.p. phaeopus*) on the coast; a few occur inland along Lower River. Probably 500–700 winter along the coast and in the coastal mangrove swamps Sep–Apr. Migrating flocks seen in Sep. Some non-breeding birds over-summer.

163. TRINGA ERYTHROPUS PV, WV

Spotted (or Dusky) Redshank

Scarce, mainly passage, Palaearctic visitor Nov and Feb–Mar, though a few winter on freshwater swamps, both near the coast and inland. Occurs singly or in parties up to 3.

164. TRINGA FLAVIPES AV

Lesser Yellowlegs

One record only of this Nearctic vagrant: a single seen at a small pool near the Wadner Beach Hotel, Banjul, 23 Jan 1976 (GOS ABR 1976) was subsequently confirmed (GOS ABR 1977, Addenda). Also recorded in Nigeria (Elgood 1982) and Ghana (Grimes 1987).

165. TRINGA GLAREOLA PV, WV

Wood Sandpiper

Common Palaearctic passage and winter visitor to marshes and ricefields throughout the country Aug–Apr, but recorded in all months. Main arrival Oct; *c.* 300 counted on Jakhaly swamp, May 1975 (GOS Rev).

166. TRINGA (=ACTITIS) HYPOLEUCOS PV, WV

Common Sandpiper

Common and widespread Palaearctic visitor, usually seen singly, sometimes parties up to 4, beside water, Aug–Apr; main arrival Sep–Oct. Non-breeding birds occasionally over-summer.

167. TRINGA (=GLOTTIS) NEBULARIA PV, WV

Greenshank

Widespread and common Palaearctic visitor, usually seen singly on mudflats in Lower River, Sep–Apr; main arrival Oct–Nov. Several hundred probably winter along the creeks in the mangrove near Banjul. Smaller numbers occur on inland swamps.

168. TRINGA OCHROPUS PV, WV

Green Sandpiper

Passage and winter Palaearctic visitor, mid Aug–early Apr. Scarce on the coast, mostly on passage Sep–Oct and Mar, but widespread and not uncommon inland on most swamps throughout the winter. Maximum together, 10 at Jakhaly, 26 Aug 1976 (GOS ABR 1976) and 32 at Baratenda, 21–22 Mar 1981 (GOS ABR 1981).

169. TRINGA (=GLOTTIS) STAGNATILIS PV, WV

Marsh Sandpiper

Uncommon Palaearctic and winter visitor on the coast, Aug–Apr, mostly Nov–Mar; maximum together, 12 around Banjul, Jan–Feb.

170. TRINGA TEREK AV

Terek Sandpiper

Vagrant from the Palaearctic, only one record: a single bird (photographed) in Lower River, 19 Dec 1974 (Jensen & Kirkeby 1980).

171. TRINGA TOTANUS PV, WV

Redshank

Common Palaearctic passage and winter visitor (*T.t. totanus* and *T.t. robusta*), usually singly or in parties of up to 6; most numerous Oct–Nov and Mar, on the coast and along Lower River in mangrove creeks. Uncommon further inland but occasionally reported from swamps at Sapu and Jakhaly.

Arenariinae

172. ARENARIA INTERPRES PV, WV

Turnstone

Common Palaearctic visitor (*A.i. interpres*) on the coast Sep–Apr, main arrival Nov; maximum together *c.* 100 off Banjul Bund in Jan, but usually in flocks up to 15. A few over-summer: *c.* 30 at Brufut, 20 Jun 1976 (GOS ABR 1976).

Phalaropodinae

173. PHALAROPUS FULICARIUS PV?

Grey Phalarope

Undoubtedly a regular offshore Palaearctic passage migrant but largely overlooked. Only 2 records: large flock (no number given) off Banjul, 27 Mar 1941 (C. A. Norris per E. M. Cawkell); 3 off Fajara, Oct 1988 (C. R. Barlow *et al.*). Recorded regularly off the coast of Senegal (Morel 1972) and common further south off the West African coast.

Gallinagoninae

174. GALLINAGO (=CAPELLA) GALLINAGO WV

Common Snipe

Not uncommon Palaearctic winter visitor (*G.g. gallinago*) to freshwater swamps throughout the country Sep–early May; most arrive Nov. Maximum together 40+ at Camaloo, Jan 1966 (Bray *et al.*).

175. GALLINAGO MEDIA AV

Great Snipe

The only record is 3 at Prufu swamp, near Chamoi, 21 Jan 1974 (Jensen & Kirkeby 1980). A rare Palaearctic visitor to West Africa, recorded from Senegal.

176. GALLINAGO (=LYMNOCRYPTES) MINIMA (WV?)

Jack Snipe

Rare Palaearctic winter visitor, only 4 records: Salekini, one shot by Lowe, 15 Jan 1929 (Bannerman 1930–51); near Soma, one flushed from a swamp in winter

1973–74 (no date given) (GOS Rev), 3 there 14 Feb 1974 (Jensen & Kirkeby 1980); Camaloo, one on 25 Nov 1978 (M. E. Smalley). Possibly a regular winter visitor since it is easily overlooked.

177. LIMNODROMUS GRISEUS/LIMNODROMUS SCOLOPACEUS AV

Short-billed Dowitcher/Long-billed Dowitcher

One record only: a bird in full breeding plumage at Camaloo, 23 Dec 1978 (see *Malimbus* (1979) 1:68) could not be specifically identified. Both are North American breeding birds which migrate south to South America in winter. The only other record for West Africa is one *L. griseus* in Ghana, Oct 1976 (*Bull. Nig. Orn. Soc.* (1977) 13 (44): 148).

Calidridinae

178. CALIDRIS (=CROCETHIA) ALBA PV, WV

Sanderling

Common Palaearctic visitor on the coast Aug–Apr. Main passage Oct and Mar; wintering birds arrive later and flocks of up to 30 occupy a half-mile stretch of beach through the winter. Most depart by early Apr, but reported until 16 May. No over-summering records.

179. CALIDRIS (=EROLIA) ALPINA PV, WV

Dunlin

Not uncommon Palaearctic passage and winter visitor (*C.a. alpina*) to coastal mudflats, Aug–Apr; most Nov–Dec. Largest flock reported *c.* 200 in Nov, but flocks of 10–30 more usual.

[CALIDRIS BAIRDII

Baird's Sandpiper

There is one record of this Nearctic species which occasionally strays across the Atlantic: a single bird, apparently photographed, off Banjul Bund, 25 Nov 1976 (Jensen & Kirkeby 1980). Not having seen the photograph and having no other details I must place it in square brackets.]

180. CALIDRIS CANUTUS PV, WV

Knot

Uncommon Palaearctic passage and winter visitor (*C.c. canutus*). Main arrival Oct; flocks of up to 30 occur on the coast intermittently Oct–Nov and Feb–Mar. A few over-winter: once *c.* 150 off Banjul Bund, 20 Dec 1975 (GOS ABR 1975).

181. CALIDRIS FERRUGINEA (=EROLIA TESTACEA) PV, WV

Curlew Sandpiper

Common Palaearctic passage and winter visitor on the coast, occurring in flocks up to 50, Sep–May, most numerous Sep–Oct and Mar.

182. CALIDRIS (=EROLIA) MINUTA PV, WV

Little Stint

Abundant Palaearctic passage and winter visitor on the coast. Several thousand present in flocks of up to 300 Oct–Nov and Feb–Apr, with smaller numbers remaining throughout the winter.

183. CALIDRIS (=EROLIA) TEMMINCKII (PV), (WV)

Temminck's Stint

Rare Palaearctic passage and winter visitor but easily overlooked among the large numbers of *C. minuta*. Only 9 records: Barra, 3 on 7 Nov 1956 (Cawkell & Moreau); Banjul Bund, one on 13 Oct 1965 (Bray *et al.*), one trapped and ringed, Dec 1969 (G. Johansen), one on 16 Jan 1983 (GOS RR); Camaloo, 3 on 27 Mar, one still present 11 Apr 1966 (Bray *et al.*), 7 in early Mar 1973 (J. N. Dymond & M. Wright), one on 4 Feb 1978 (C. V. Eyre); Cape Lagoon, one on 19 May 1974 (GOS Rev); Keneba, one on 20 Nov 1977 (GOS ABR 1977).

[TRYNGITES SUBRUFICOLLIS Rejected

Buff-breasted Sandpiper

A record of one on a rubbish tip near the Wadner Beach Hotel, Banjul, on 8 Dec 1984 seems possible as there have been a number of North American vagrants reported in West Africa in recent years. This species has occurred in Tunisia, Sierra Leone, Egypt and Kenya (Brown *et al.* 1986), and Ghana (Grimes 1987). It was not, however, accepted because of the possibility of confusion with a female *Philomachus pugnax* (GOS RR).]

184. PHILOMACHUS PUGNAX PV, WV

Ruff

Locally abundant Palaearctic passage and winter visitor, late Jul to late Apr, on freshwater marches and ricefields throughout the country. Main arrival Sep–Oct. Up to 5000 reported at Soma and Jakhaly, Jan–Mar.

STERCORARIIDAE

[STERCORARIUS LONGICAUDATUS Rejected

Long-tailed Skua

A report of one off Cape St Mary in Dec 1983 has been submitted without details but has not been accepted as it could refer to *P. pomarinus* (GOS RR).]

185. STERCORARIUS PARASITICUS PV

Richardson's (or Arctic) Skua

Holarctic passage visitor off the coast, probably regular, but rarely seen. Singles near Gunjur, 29 Aug 1961 (Cawkell & Moreau), off Cape St Mary, 10 Oct 1965 (Bray *et al.*), 19 Oct 1973 (GOS Rev) and a dark phase bird over the river off Albreda, 18 Dec 1979 (R. Hume, D. Fisher). Several records of unidentified skuas may relate to this species.

186. STERCORARIUS POMARINUS PV

Pomatorhine (or Pomarine) Skua

Probably occurs regularly off the coast on passage from the Palaearctic. Few records: off Cape St Mary, singles on 10 Oct 1965 (Bray *et al.*), 19 Oct 1975 (GOS ABR 1975), 4 Apr 1983 (GOS RR); near Buoy No 1, one on 1 Dec 1974 (GOS Rev); Banjul, one on 19 Mar 1976; an apparently sick bird at Brufut, 4 Jul 1976 (GOS ABR 1976); off Barra, 2 on 30 Jan 1984 (GOS RR).

LARIDAE
Larinae

187. LARUS ARGENTATUS (=ATLANTIS) WV

Herring Gull

Rare visitor to the coast, most presumably being the Atlantic Is. race *L.a. atlantis*. Singles near Banjul on 1 Jan, 24 Mar, 30 May 1966 (Bray *et al.*), Nov 1968 (GOS Rev), 11 Dec 1975 (GOS ABR 1975); Brufut, 2 on 20 Aug 1974, one on 6 Apr 1975 (GOS Rev), one on 17 Dec 1975 (GOS ABR 1975); Cape St Mary, one on 13 Dec 1975 (GOS ABR 1975); Camaloo, 5 on 17 Dec 1975 and 2 at Kartung, on the same day (GOS ABR 1975). One at Cape Lagoon, 16 Dec 1987 with flesh-coloured legs was presumably the nominate race (W. E. Waters). The only other recent records are both unconfirmed: a single off Cape St Mary, 4 Apr 1983 and 2 off Barra, 30 Jan 1984 (GOS RR).

188. LARUS ATRICILLA AV

Laughing Gull

Two records only of this North American vagrant: single adult on a wrecked groundnutter off Banjul Bund, 5 Dec 1983 and a first winter bird at Cape Lagoon, 27 Feb 1984 (GOS RR). Previously reported from Morocco (Brown *et al.* 1986) and possibly hybridising with a *L. cirrocephalus* in colony at the Saloum delta, Senegal, 1983 (Erard *et al.* 1984).

189. LARUS AUDOUINII AV

Audouin's Gull

A vagrant from the Mediterranean, only 4 records (all singles): Cape Lagoon, 21 Feb 1982, Feb (no date given) 1984; Barra, 30 Jan 1984; Banjul Bund, 9 Feb 1984 (GOS RR).

190. LARUS CANUS AV

Common Gull

Vagrant from the Palaearctic to coastal waters, two records only: single adult off Bund Road, 25 Sep 1984 and a first winter bird at Cape Lagoon, 4 Jan 1986 (GOS RR).

191. LARUS CIRROCEPHALUS RB

Grey-headed Gull

Common resident on the coast, probably nests on some of the swampy flats along the many mangrove creeks but there are no recent breeding records.

Hopkinson (Bannerman 1930–51) reported 2 colonies in Niumi province — one on swampy flats between the coast and Jennak creek, the other on a flat island among mangroves of the Sika creek. Walton stated they bred on the Bijilo Is. in Jul (Cawkell & Moreau). Copulation seen on Banjul Bund in Jul (GOS Rev) and at Camaloo in May (GOS ABR 1977).

192. LARUS FUSCUS — WV

Lesser Black-backed Gull

Common winter visitor (*L.f. graellsii*) from the Palaearctic on the coast late Aug–early May.

193. LARUS GENEI — WV

Slender-billed Gull

Uncommon but regular off-season visitor on the coast, probably from the colony in Senegal on L'ile de Diamanio, l'embouchure du Saloum. Only 10 records until 1976 but since then reported annually, Nov–May.

194. LARUS MELANOCEPHALUS — AV

Mediterranean Gull

Vagrant from the Mediterranean, only 6 records (all singles and mostly first winter birds): Camaloo, 27 Dec 1975; Banjul, 29 Dec 1975 (Jensen & Kirkeby 1980), 28 Dec 1982, 27 Dec 1983 and 24 Jan 1984 (GOS RR); adult at Cape St Mary, Nov 1977 (Jensen & Kirkeby 1980). Has been recorded from the coast of Senegal.

195. LARUS MINUTUS — AV

Little Gull

Three records: an immature at Kotu Stream, 14 Nov 1977, a second-winter bird off Banjul Bund, 17 Nov 1977 (Jensen & Kirkeby 1980) and one there, 25 Sep 1984 (Morel & Morel in prep.). A rare Palaearctic visitor to West Africa.

196. LARUS PIPIXCAN — AV

Franklin's Gull

There are 2 sightings of this North American species: a first winter bird off Banjul Bund, 1–2 Feb 1984 and another (possibly the same bird) at Cape Lagoon in the same month. Both have been accepted on the basis of detailed descriptions (GOS RR). (One paired with a *L. cirrocephalus* in the colony at the Saloum delta, Senegal in 1983 (Erard *et al.* 1984).

197. LARUS RIDIBUNDUS — WV

Black-headed Gull

Uncommon but regular Palaearctic winter visitor to the coast. Most records are Nov–May, once Jun. Maximum reported, 15–20 at Banjul, 12 Jan 1975 (GOS ABR 1975).

198. LARUS TRIDACTYLUS AV

Kittiwake

Vagrant from the northern Palaearctic, one record only: an immature at Cape Lagoon on 21 Dec 1975 (GOS ABR 1975). Previously recorded occasionally from the Senegal coast.

Sterninae

199. ANOUS STOLIDUS AV

(Common) Noddy

Vagrant from the South Atlantic, one record only: a sick bird, which had been picked up by a child on the beach at Brufut, was examined in the hand on 6 Aug 1974 and died a few minutes later (GOS Rev).

200. ANOUS MINUTUS (=TENUIROSTRIS) AV

Black (or White-capped) Noddy

Vagrant from the South Atlantic, two confirmed records only: a single bird, watched for 5 minutes from a boat at 10 m range, fishing with *c*. 300 *Sterna nigra* off Cape St Mary, 13 Oct 1977; probably the same bird was seen flying north 150 m offshore at Fajara, 30 Oct 1977 and several times off Bakau in early Nov (GOS ABR 1977); one with flock of *Sterna nigra* off Cape St Mary, 14 Nov 1984. This was originally not accepted (GOS RR) as insufficient details were available but a full description has now been published (Ericsson 1989) and the record is acceptable.

201. STERNA ALBIFRONS PV, (RB)

Little Tern

One breeding record of the resident West African race *S.a. guinea*: 2 adults feeding 2 young near Banjul Bund, 22 Aug 1966 (Bray *et al*.). Flocks which occur on passage Sep–Nov and Mar–May are almost certainly the nominate Palaearctic race (*S.a. albifrons*). Maximum reported, over 100 off Banjul, 17 May 1965 (Bray *et al*.). There was a noticeable passage off Cape St Mary, Mar–Apr 1976 and Nov 1977 (GOS ABR 1976–77).

202. STERNA BENGALENSIS WV

Lesser Crested Tern

Scarce but regular winter visitor on the coast; most records are from Cape Lagoon where up to 20 recorded Sep–Apr annually since 1973. Earliest, 6 on 20 Aug 1977; maximum 20, early Nov 1977 (GOS ABR 1975–76–77). Also recorded from Barra, Banjul Bund and Denton Bridge. Previously presumably overlooked among the large numbers of *S. maxima*. Birds were observed moving south off the coast of Morocco from late Sep to late Oct 1962–63 by Smith (*Ibis* 107: 493), but The Gambia appears to have been previously unrecognised as a wintering ground for part of the Mediterranean population.

203. STERNA DOUGALLII AV, ?PV

Roseate Tern

Surprisingly there is only one confirmed record: a bird photographed at Cape St Mary, 17 Jul 1966 (A. Vittery). There are several probable sightings and it is likely that this species is a regular passage migrant along the coast (common on the Liberian coast, Aug–Sep and Mar (M. E. J. Gore)) but is overlooked among the large numbers of migrating terns; they may, however, pass The Gambia in off-shore waters out of sight of land. (See note under *S. paradisaea* for which there are also surprisingly few records.)

[STERNA FUSCATA Rejected

Sooty Tern

The record of 2 at Cape St Mary, 17 Jan 1973 (Jensen & Kirkeby 1980) and included in Morel & Morel (in prep.) was not accepted by the G.O.S.]

204. STERNA HIRUNDO PV

Common Tern

Rare passage visitor (*S.h. hirundo*) in small numbers mostly on the coast and in Lower River. Several at Basse, Jan 1976 (M. E. J. Gore) is the only record from up-river. There are large colonies in Mauritania and Western Sahara and a small colony in Senegal on L'ile de Diamanio, l'embouchure du Saloum (Morel 1972) and doubtless some of these birds stray into The Gambia but there are few recent records. Two positively identified amongst flock of *c.* 30 similar terns at Cape Lagoon, 14 Dec 1988 and one, probably several, in the same area, 15 Dec 1989 (W. E. Waters). Presumably most of the Palaearctic migrants pass The Gambia out of sight of land.

205. STERNA HYBRIDA (=CHLIDONIAS LEUCOPAREIA) PV, WV

Whiskered Tern

Scarce Palaearctic passage and winter visitor (*S.h. hybrida*) singly and in small parties around Banjul, Jul–Apr, once Jun; maximum 14 at Cape Lagoon, 19 Feb 1975 (GOS ABR 1975). Only records from up-river are *c.* 30 at Pakalinding, 12 Jan 1969 (GOS Rev) and 2 at Tendaba, 23 Feb 1975 (GOS ABR 1975). Hopkinson (Bannerman 1930–51) considered it to be the most numerous of the wintering marsh terns, more common than *S. nigra*, which is certainly not the case today and his identification may be in doubt.

206. STERNA (=CHLIDONIAS) LEUCOPTERA PV

White-winged Black Tern

Palaearctic mainly northward passage visitor in substantial numbers (Mar–Apr) on the coast when birds coming into breeding plumage are very noticeable. Presumably on southward migration the birds migrate further inland for there is only one autumn record on the coast: a single on 12 Sep 1965 (Bray *et al.*); occasionally reported in winter. Maximum *c.* 70 off Banjul Bund, 22 Apr 1976 (GOS ABR 1976). Up-river records are few: *c.* 30 on the river between the coast and 240 km inland, 6–8 Mar 1976 (GOS ABR 1976) and one at Georgetown, 26 Nov 1987 (J. N. Dymond); it seems certain it has been overlooked inland.

207. STERNA MAXIMA RB*, FB

Royal Tern

Present (*S.m. albididorsalis*) on the coast in hundreds, with tens occurring inland along Lower River to about Tendaba, throughout the year. Probably breeds but no nesting colony now known. Two pairs were breeding on the Bijilo Is., Jul 1948 (Cawkell & Moreau). Breeds on islands off the coast of Casamance, a few miles south of The Gambia (Morel 1972).

208. STERNA (=CHLIDONIAS) NIGRA PV, WV

Black Tern

Abundant Palaearctic passage and winter visitor (*S.n. nigra*) to the coast. Several flocks up to 1000 recorded offshore Jul–May, most Aug–Oct and Mar. One or two flocks of 50–80 non-breeding birds usually over-summer at Denton Bridge and Cape St Mary.

209. STERNA (=GELOCHELIDON) NILOTICA WV

Gull-billed Tern

Scarce winter visitor (*S.n. nilotica*) on the coast; recorded also inland along Lower River as far east as Tendaba. Most records are Sep–Apr, but has been recorded in every month.

210. STERNA PARADISAEA PV

Arctic Tern

Rare Palaearctic passage visitor on the coast, Apr–May and Sep. Surprisingly few records, either because they are overlooked among the large numbers of other terns and are not separated from the very similar *S. hirundo* or because they mainly migrate at sea out of sight of land. Only 7 records: 7 recorded during May 1965 and 7 during Apr and May 1966 (A. Vittery); an unspecified number seen from a ship 5 miles offshore, 29 Sep 1967 (GOS Rev) and 'small numbers 7 May–3 Jul (photo)' (Bray *et al.*) (the Jun–Jul birds presumably being non-breeders over-summering); 27 circling over Camaloo in late afternoon, 15 Apr 1977 (GOS ABR 1977); singles off Banjul Bund, 15 Apr 1983 and Denton Bridge, 8 Apr 1984 (GOS RR).

211. STERNA SANDVICENSIS PV, WV

Sandwich Tern

Common passage and winter Palaearctic visitor (*S.s. sandvicensis*) on the coast, with flocks up to 40 recorded between Sep and May. Total wintering population numbers several hundred. A few over-summer.

212. STERNA TSCHEGRAVA (=HYDROPROGNE CASPIA) RB

Caspian Tern

Resident and common on the coast. The nesting colony on the Bijilo Is. (Cawkell & Moreau) which was deserted when the islands were inundated in the 1950s has been re-established since 1986: *c.* 150 pairs, Aug 1989 (C. R. Barlow). Hopkinson believed they bred on a small mangrove island off the mouth of the Sami (Sika) (Bannerman 1930–51) but there are no known colonies there now. There are breeding colonies on islands in the Saloum delta a few miles to the north, and Casamance to the south, of The Gambia (Morel 1972).

RYNCHOPIDAE

213. RYNCHOPS FLAVIROSTRIS AfM

African Skimmer (or Scissor-billed Tern)

Intra-African migrant; scarce non-breeding visitor, mainly towards the end of the dry season, but recorded most months. Maximum reported, 18 at Camaloo and Banjul Bund, 29 Jun 1969 (GOS Rev). Cawkell (1965) had 6 records Jun–Aug and one in Jan. Singles at Basse, Nov 1972 (E. Edberg), Yellitenda, 28 May, Cape Lagoon, 8 Jun 1975 (GOS ABR 1975), Camaloo, 4 Jul 1976 (GOS ABR 1976) and Barra, 27 Mar 1977 (GOS ABR 1977). Reported most years since 1980.

PTEROCLIDIDAE

214. PTEROCLES EXUSTUS AV

Chestnut-bellied Sandgrouse

Status uncertain, probably a rare and occasional visitor (*P.e. exustus*) to the eastern part of the country. Hopkinson never recorded it, but Bannerman (1930–51) considered it probably occurred since it is recorded from Casamance, Senegal. Cawkell had very few records, all from Basse (Cawkell & Moreau). No acceptable records (*pace* Jensen & Kirkeby 1980) until 10 Mar 1989 when one was observed near Bansang (R. Webzall).

215. PTEROCLES QUADRICINCTUS RB

Four-banded Sandgrouse

Locally common resident in dry open country, sometimes in open woodland, most numerous in Middle and Upper River. Some occur in open scrub bordering the sand-dunes on the coast, but not common elsewhere in Lower River. Breeds Dec–Apr: hatching at Brufut, 24 Mar 1975; pair with 2 young just able to fly, 30 Mar 1975 (GOS ABR 1975); nest C/3 in same area, 27 Mar 1977 (GOS ABR 1977); breeding recorded at Basse, Dec 1987 (C. R. Barlow).

COLUMBIDAE

216. COLUMBA GUINEA RB

Speckled Pigeon

Common resident (*C.g. guinea*) on the coast and inland where there are plantations of rhun palm *Borassus aethiopium*. Breeds commonly on buildings at Banjul and its environs, but elsewhere normally nests in rhun palms. Probably breeds throughout the year, though mostly immediately after the rains Nov–Mar.

217. OENA CAPENSIS DSV

Long-tailed (or Namaqua) Dove

Common dry season visitor, widely distributed in open country from late Oct to Jun; shows a preference for the verges of dusty tracks. May occasionally breed: a young bird was seen at Banjul Bund, 20 Mar (E. M. Cawkell) and juveniles seen at Tendaba, Nov 1987 (C. R. Barlow).

218. STREPTOPELIA DECIPIENS RB*

Mourning Dove

Common resident (*S.d. shelleyi*) in open country with scattered trees, agricultural land, in Middle and Upper River, where it largely replaces *S. semitorquata*. Scarce on the coast, small parties of up to 6 occurring there immediately after the rains, Nov–Jan, when dispersal presumably occurs. Surprisingly there are no breeding records.

219. STREPTOPELIA ROSEOGRISEA RB?

Rose-grey (or Pink-headed) Dove

Status uncertain; previously considered a local and scarce resident (*S.r. roseogrisea*) in the vicinity of towns and villages in Lower River, largely overlooked because of its similarity to *S. vinacea*. Recorded in the Banjul area and at Yundum (GOS Rev, GOS ABR 1977). These may, however, have been domestic 'Barbary Doves'. The only recent record appears to be 4 near Basse, 22 Nov 1984 (Ericsson 1989) closer to the semi-desert zone in Senegal where it is common (Morel & Morel in prep.).

220. STREPTOPELIA SEMITORQUATA RB

Red-eyed Dove

Abundant resident in Lower River; occurs throughout the country, but less common inland, where it is largely replaced by *S. decipiens*. Breeds Dec–Apr, usually C/2.

221. STREPTOPELIA (=STIGMATOPELIA) SENEGALENSIS RB

Laughing Dove

Resident (*S.s. senegalensis*) and common in the vicinity of towns and villages. Appears to breed throughout the year.

222. STREPTOPELIA TURTUR PV

European Turtle-Dove

Irregularly abundant (*S.t. turtur*) Palaearctic passage visitor in Middle River, Feb–Mar in some years during the 1970s; very few in other years and subsequently. Stragglers occur on the coast in spring. Large flocks first reported in 1973. Records of uncountable numbers, certainly over one million, in Mar passing over the river to roost near Kaur, Feb 1976 and in hundreds of thousands at Jakhaly swamp, Feb–Mar 1975 and 1976 (GOS Rev, GOS ABR 1975–76). Large numbers again at Jakhaly, Mar 1977 with hundreds still present early May (GOS ABR 1977), but very few reported in 1974, 1978 and 1979; *c.* 10,000 at Kaur, 25 Mar 1980 (GOS ABR 1980) but few records since until considerable numbers reported, Jan 1989 (P. Byass). The species is declining in Europe, largely as a result of excessive shooting in Mediterranean countries during migration periods, particularly in spring which reduces breeding populations. This may explain the lack of recent records. Always rare on southward migration with occasional records of small parties on the coast, Sep–Nov.

223. STREPTOPELIA VINACEA RB

Vinaceous Dove

Abundant resident in open agricultural land. Breeds throughout the dry season, possibly throughout the year.

224. TRERON (= VINAGO) AUSTRALIS RB

Green Fruit-Pigeon

Resident and not uncommon (*T.a. nudirostris*) in small numbers in open woodland mostly in Lower River. Local movements occur as the fruits of different species of trees on which they feed ripen. Numbers have decreased considerably this century, probably largely due to the excessive felling of the forest in Lower River, though shooting may have been a contributory factor. Rendall (1892) stated that 'during the rainy season there seems to be a constant flow from the south-west. Incredible numbers are shot . . .'. Now only seen in parties of 6–8, mainly near the coast. Breeding recorded Mar–Apr.

225. TRERON (= VINAGO) WAALIA RB

Yellow-bellied Fruit-Pigeon (or Bruce's Green Pigeon)

Resident and not uncommon in open country with scattered trees, inland from Kiang West to the eastern end of the country. Only 2 records from near the coast: one at Fajara, Feb 1974 (GOS Rev) and one with a flock of *T. australis* at Tanji, Dec 1988 (C. R. Barlow). Breeds Dec–Apr.

226. TURTUR ABYSSINICUS RB

Black-billed (Blue-spotted) Wood-Dove

Common resident; occurs throughout the country in woodland, but appears to be most numerous in Middle and Upper River. Only breeding record is Mar. See under *T. afer*.

227. TURTUR AFER RB

Red-Billed (or Blue-spotted) Wood-Dove

Resident and abundant in open woodland, most numerous in Lower River, but overlaps everywhere with the very similar *T. abyssinicus* and both species appear to occur throughout the country. Breeds during and immediately after the rains, Oct–Jan, usually C/2.

PSITTACIDAE

228. POICEPHALUS ROBUSTUS RB

Brown-necked Parrot

Scarce, local resident (*P.r. fuscicollis*), found mainly in the belt of high mangrove, *Rhizophora*, which borders the river between Pirang and Sambang on the south bank. Occasionally flocks may be encountered in high open woodland, but rarely far from the river or from mangrove-lined creeks. Nests in holes high in the mangrove. Breeding starts Mar or Apr but may be extended as pair observed guarding a hole in a baobab tree at Pirang in Oct (G.G.F.P.). Numbers appear to be declining.

229. POICEPHALUS SENEGALUS RB

Senegal (or Yellow-bellied) Parrot

Common resident (*P.s. senegalus*) in open woodland and cleared agricultural land with scattered trees throughout the country. All-yellow morphs occasionally reported. Breeding season appears to be extended: copulation observed at Camaloo in Jan (GOS Rev); unfledged young being offered for sale at Kwinella in Jun; pair nesting in hole 10 m up in tree at Fajara in Oct, and flying young observed there in Sep (M. E. J. Gore).

230. PSITTACULA KRAMERI RB

Senegal Long-tailed (or Rose-ringed) Parrakeet

Common resident (*P.k. krameri*) widely distributed throughout the country in open agricultural land with scattered trees. Breeds during the dry season, Dec–May: pair attempting to take over the nest-hole of *Phoeniculus purpureus* in Dec; young offered for sale in May.

MUSOPHAGIDAE

231 CRINIFER PISCATOR RB

Grey Plantain-eater

Common resident in open woodland, gardens and on the edge of forest throughout the country; a familiar garden bird at Fajara. Breeding recorded Oct–May.

232. MUSOPHAGA VIOLACEA RB

Violet Plantain-eater (or Touraco)

Resident, widely distributed but scarce and probably decreasing, in the little remaining forest throughout the country. Birds move to wherever fig trees are fruiting. Eggs C/2, in Apr (Cawkell & Moreau) is the only breeding record but display observed in Dec (C. R. Barlow).

233. TAURACO (=TURACUS) PERSA RB*

Green-crested (or Guinea) Touraco

Scarce and local resident (*T.p. buffoni*), apparently confined to the remaining small area of high forest in Lower River at Abuko, Brikama, Pirang, Brufut, Tanji and Selety. Present in Abuko Nature Reserve throughout the year and undoubtedly breeds, but no nest has ever been found.

CUCULIDAE
Cuculinae

234. CHRYSOCOCCYX (=LAMPROMORPHA) CAPRIUS MB

Didric Cuckoo

Not uncommon breeding visitor widely distributed in open woodland before and during the rains, Jun–Nov. Courtship observed in Jun and Jul. Bannerman (1930–51) cites 28 species on which it is known to be parasitic in West Africa, mostly weavers and finches, but no young have been seen being fed in The Gambia and the foster species there are not known.

235. CHRYSOCOCCYX CUPREUS — AV, FB?

Emerald Cuckoo

There is only one record this century: a single at Brufut, 14 Jul 1981 (GOS ABR 1981). There is a reference to this species in The Gambia by Rendall (1892), who wrote 'The most beautiful bird I saw on the West Coast; its skins, I regret to say, find a ready sale on The Gambia, owing to the hateful traffic created by the French plumassiers' which doubtless explains its present rarity, though deforestation has contributed to its decline. (Formerly common in Casamance, Senegal, but the only recent record is one near Ziguinchor, 2 Aug 1968 (Morel 1972)).

236. CHRYSOCOCCYX (=LAMPROMORPHA) KLAAS — DSV

Klaas' Cuckoo

Not uncommon dry season visitor in open woodland and open bush throughout the country; mostly Oct–Feb, but once 3 Jun and one Jul record. Courtship has never been observed and there is no evidence of breeding.

237. CLAMATOR GLANDARIUS — RB, WV, AfM

Great-spotted Cuckoo

Scarce resident (probably partially migratory) and winter visitor in open bush on the edge of cleared agricultural land throughout the country, augmented by migrants from southern Europe and North Africa in autumn. In West Africa appears to be mainly parasitic on Pied Crows *Corvus albus* (Serle *et al.*) which breed Apr–Jun. Copulation observed at Camaloo, 16 May 1966 (Bray *et al.*); juveniles seen begging food from pair of Pied Crows, 28 Aug 1966 (E. M. Cawkell). Juveniles disperse after fledging and in some years, e.g. 1977 and 1978, are quite common near the coast, Jul–Aug, though some of these may be early Palaearctic migrants.

238. CLAMATOR JACOBINUS — RB?

Pied Crested (or Black-and-White) Cuckoo

Status uncertain. Hopkinson believed it to be resident (*C.j. pica*) but rare, increasing in numbers during the rains, identifying one probably on MacCarthy I. and others 'often along the river' (Bannerman 1930–51). Very few records (all singles) since the 1920s: Barokunda, 2 Dec 1965 (Bray *et al.*), Jakhaly, mid-Nov; Abuko, 12 Dec; Bakau, 13 Dec; Soma, 15 and 22 Dec 1975 (GOS ABR 1975). Since 1976 there have been 9 sightings (7 inland, 2 on the coast); on one of these more than 12 individuals were flushed from tall reeds at Sapu, 28 Nov 1980 (GOS ABR 1980).

239. CLAMATOR LEVAILLANTII — MB

Levaillant's Cuckoo

Common breeding visitor in open woodland and gardens, just before and during the rains, Jun–Nov, when it is parasitic mainly on *Turdoides reinwardii*. Young have also been seen being fed by *T. plebejus* and *Spreo pulcher*.

240. CUCULUS CANORUS (=GULARIS) MB, WV, AfM

Common Cuckoo

The resident African race, *C.c. gularis*, is difficult to separate in the field from the nominate Palaearctic race which winters in Africa except by the distinctive call. *C.c. gularis* appears to be an intra-African wanderer arriving shortly before the start of the rains in May–Jun; several individuals were seen at Brufut in open woodland apparently searching for nests, Jun–Jul, 1976 and 1977 (M. E. J. Gore). At this time of the year it is most in evidence, which is the start of the breeding season for most passerines on which it is parasitic. Recorded in every month except Jan and Feb. Some winter records presumably relate to Palaearctic migrants, but the only positive identification of *C.c. canorus* was 27 Mar (no year given) by Hopkinson, who collected one of the African race the same day (Bannerman 1930–51).

241. CUCULUS CLAMOSUS AV

Black Cuckoo

Rare African vagrant; one (*C.c. clamosus*) collected by Rendall, 6 Sep 1889, appears to be the only confirmed record. Hopkinson reported that, although he never saw this species himself, a Mr Pryce described it to him and said it was occasionally seen in Niumi at the start of the rains (Bannerman 1930–51). Jensen & Kirkeby (1980) have a doubtful record of a juvenile at Kerewan, 11 Feb 1976.

242. CUCULUS SOLITARIUS AV

Red-chested Cuckoo

Intra-African migrant, only 9 records (all singles): Kudang, late Aug 1963 (Cawkell 1965); Abuko Nature Reserve, 15 Jul 1964, 27 Sep 1964, 23 Jul 1973 (GOS Rev), 11 Dec 1975 (GOS ABR 1975), 23 Oct 1979; Brufut, 22 May 1979 (GOS ABR 1979); Yundum, 30 Aug 1980; Wallikunda, Aug 1980 (GOS ABR 1980). There have been no confirmed sightings since.

Phaenicophaeinae

243. CEUTHMOCHARES AEREUS

Yellowbill Coucal

Bannerman (1930–51) states that the Upper Guinea race *C.a. flavirostris* is recorded from The Gambia, adding that it is evidently scarce, but gives no details. Only one recent record: a single bird in thick cover fringing woodland at Jabang, 4 May 1963 (E. M. Cawkell). There is also a likely but unconfirmed record of one at Pirang, May 1985 (G.G.F.P.).

Centropodinae

244. CENTROPUS SENEGALENSIS RB

Senegal Coucal

Common resident (*C.s. senegalensis*), widely distributed in open country and scrub, often in gardens. Breeds Jul–Nov, usually C/3–5.

245. CENTROPUS TOULOU (=GRILLII) RB

Black Coucal

Scarce resident (*C.t. grillii*), confined to grassland bordering freshwater swamps. First recorded 10 Aug 1948 (Cawkell & Moreau) but not mentioned by Bannerman (1953). Seen annually, mostly in Middle River in suitable habitat from Baboon I. to Georgetown; pair seen carrying nesting material at Jakhaly, 29 Aug 1963 (Cawkell 1965) and pairs were observed early Aug and 25 Oct 1974 (GOS Rev). Recorded at Mansakonko, 21 Sep 1974 (GOS Rev) and from the coast once in spring 1960 (no date) and at Cape St Mary, 22 Sep 1981 (GOS ABR 1981). The range of *C.t. grillii* given by White does not include The Gambia and he admits no other races in Africa.

TYTONIDAE

246. TYTO ALBA RB

Barn Owl

Recorded (*T.a. affinis*) from Banjul and environs, where it is not uncommon, and Basse where a pair was present in the roof of a house in 1980 (GOS ABR 1980). Probably also occurs in other larger townships inland. Breeds Dec–Mar; 3 young, recently hatched, in roof of house at Fajara in Mar 1976. (GOS ABR 1976). Numbers are increasing in periurban areas.

STRIGIDAE
Buboninae

247. BUBO AFRICANUS ?RB

Spotted Eagle-Owl

Rare, probably resident, apparently having arrived in The Gambia in the last decade. First reported in 1979. Only 9 records (all singles, some of which were found dead): Fajara, 12 Jul, 4 Aug and 31 Jul 1979 (GOS ABR 1979); Upper River, 31 Aug 1979 (GOS ABR 1979); Basse, Jul 1983; Abuko, Jul 1983, Feb 1985 and Dec 1985 (GOS RR); Bakau, 15 Sep 1987 (C. R. Barlow). A widely distributed owl of the savanna; recorded from Senegal.

248. BUBO LACTEUS RB

Milky (or Verreaux's) Eagle-Owl

Uncommon resident, widely distributed in relic forest. Recorded from Cape St Mary, Abuko Nature Reserve (where it is a resident breeder), Selety, Jakhaly (seen on many occasions in widely separated sections of forest adjoining the swamp, 1975–78 — M. E. J. Gore), Bansang and Basse. Breeding recorded Dec–Feb.

249. GLAUCIDIUM PERLATUM RB

Pearl-spotted Owlet

Resident and not uncommon (*G.p. perlatum*); widely distributed in open woodland throughout the country. Recorded from Cape St Mary Agricultural Department Gardens on numerous occasions, also at Yundum, in high forest near Jakhaly, and at Yoroberikunda. Only breeding record is in hole in tree *c.* 7 m off the ground in Apr 1962 and Apr 1963, C/3 (Bray *et al.*, GOS Rev).

250. OTUS (=PTILOPSIS) LEUCOTIS RB

White-faced (Scops) Owl

Not uncommon resident (*O.l. leucotis*), probably occurring throughout the country in open woodland, but to date only recorded in Lower River. Breeds at the end of the rains and the beginning of the dry season, Oct–Jan; unfledged young being found in Jan. After breeding, loose flocks sometimes occur — *c.* 13 were disturbed from a day roost in acacia trees near the coast at Brufut on several occasions 17–27 Jul 1976 (GOS ABR 1976).

251. OTUS SCOPS (=SENEGALENSIS) RB

(African) Scops Owl

Resident (*O.s. senegalensis*) and probably not uncommon, but rarely reported. Heard and seen frequently in the Fajara and Yundum area, and recorded in several places in Middle and Upper River. Only breeding record is an immature seen at Cape St Mary, 23 Aug 1966.

252. SCOTOPELIA PELI RB*

Pel's Fishing Owl

Rare resident along the river, few records: Baboon Is. (twice) and Kai Hai I. (GOS Rev, GOS ABR 1976); Tendaba, no dates (P. Aronsson); Basse, Mar 1987 (GOS ABR 1986–87); Kuntaur, 2 Jan 1988 (P. Donnelly). No nesting records, but it is sedentary and undoubtedly breeds.

Striginae

253. ASIO CAPENSIS (WSV)

African Marsh Owl

Intra-African migrant; scarce and local, irregular wet season visitor. Until 1977 there were only two records: one observed by Hopkinson in 1911 and a single bird near Banjul, 17 Oct 1970 (Morel 1972). In 1977 several appeared on the marsh at Camaloo in early Aug, reaching a maximum of 25–30 on 16 Aug and remaining until 25 Aug (GOS ABR 1977). Similar numbers appeared at Camaloo, Jul–Nov 1978, 1979 (*Malimbus* (1983) 5: 31–33), 1980 (GOS ABR 1980), 1981, 1982 (M. E. Smalley) and 1985 (B. K. Wright) when 45 were present. Since then they have appeared intermittently and in very small numbers. (See also under *A. flammeus*.)

[ASIO FLAMMEUS Rejected

Short-eared Owl

The 4 records claimed for this species must be considered doubtful and are more likely to have been *A. capensis*. Singles sighted as follows: Banjul Bund, 26 Sep 1965; Camaloo, 24 Dec 1972 (GOS Rev), 8 Jan 1974; Cape St Mary, 21 Jan 1974 (Jensen & Kirkeby 1980).]

CAPRIMULGIDAE
Caprimulginae

254. CAPRIMULGUS (=SCOTORNIS) CLIMACURUS MB*

Long-tailed Nightjar

Status uncertain, probably mainly a breeding visitor (though breeding has never been proved), but there are records throughout the year. Bannerman

(1930–51) considered that the nominate race bred in the semi-arid belt from Senegal and The Gambia eastwards, migrating south after breeding. It breeds in Senegal Mar–Jul, mostly in May (Morel 1972). Most records are Sep–Dec, with more than 100 counted in brilliant moonlight along a 300 km stretch of road, 16–17 Nov 1958 (Cawkell 1960) which suggests dispersal during the rains. Records during the probable breeding season are: near Soma, 10 disturbed from day roost, Jun 1973 (GOS Rev); near Brufut, one on 20 Apr 1976 and 6 there, 17 Apr 1978 (M. E. J. Gore); Fajara, 23 Apr 1979 (GOS ABR 1979), 4 Jul 1981 (GOS ABR 1981); Farafenni, 12 Apr 1981 (GOS ABR 1981), and Kuntaur, Jan–Mar 1989 (P. Donnelly and B. Macdonald).

255. CAPRIMULGUS EUROPAEUS WV

(European) Nightjar

Palaearctic winter visitor (*C.e. europaeus*), probably regular in open bush but overlooked and there are only 3 records since Hopkinson's day when it was reported common in winter (Bannerman 1930–51). The recent records are: Pakalinding, one on 18 Jan 1970 (O. Andrew); Jappeni, one in Jan 1972 (GOS Rev); Kotu Beach, 2 on 3 Jan 1976 (GOS ABR 1976).

256. CAPRIMULGUS NATALENSIS AV

White-tailed Nightjar

African vagrant; only record is 2 males 'chucking' beside swamp near Basse (tape-recorded), 18 Mar 1975 (Jensen & Kirkeby 1980). A bird of marshy patches in open savanna recorded from Mali to Cameroon.

[CAPRIMULGUS PECTORALIS (=NIGRISCAPULARIS)

Black-shouldered (or Dusky) Nightjar

Possibly a rare resident. Cawkell found a 'nest' with one egg of a small and very dark brown species of nightjar on laterite in open bush at Sapu in May 1960 (Cawkell & Moreau). Both birds were present and very tame but he stated that he could not be certain of their identity. There are no other records. The species is known to occur in Guinea Bissau.]

257. MACRODIPTERYX LONGIPENNIS RB, ?MB

Standard-wing Nightjar

Resident and not uncommon in open grassland and cleared agricultural land. Only breeding records are Jun–Jul, C/1, in Lower River, but males have been seen in nuptial plumage from Dec to Jul. Some dispersal away from The Gambia during the rains is probable.

258. MACRODIPTERYX (=COSMETORNIS) VEXILLARIUS AV

Pennant-winged Nightjar

Intra-African migrant; two records only: a bird examined in the hand by P. Aronsson near Soma, 4 Nov 1977 (Jensen & Kirkeby 1980) and one at Tendaba, 2 Apr 1981 (GOS ABR 1981). Breeds south of the equator and migrates north in the off-season to lat 8°N, and as vagrant further north; has been recorded in Casamance, Senegal (Bannerman 1953).

APODIDAE

259. APUS (=COLLETOPTERA) AFFINIS — RB

Little African Swift

Abundant resident (*A.a. affinis*), breeding in colonies of 5 to several hundred pairs in Banjul and the larger townships. There is a large colony beneath Denton Bridge. Nesting colonies are occupied twice during the year, Jan–Feb and Jul–Aug; appears to disperse away from the towns during the rest of the year.

260. APUS (=MICROPUS) APUS — PV

European Swift

Common (*A.a. apus*) passage migrant from the Palaearctic. First arrivals appear late Jun and flocks of several hundred occur intermittently until mid-Nov, moving south along the coast and inland along the river. Most numerous Aug–Sep, fewer occur on return passage Mar–Apr. Occasionally reported in winter.

261. APUS CAFFER — AV (FB)

White-rumped Swift

African vagrant once recorded as having bred; four birds reported as nesting under the bridge at Nema, 4 Jul 1971 by O. Andrew (Jensen & Kirkeby 1980), but not reported there since. The only other records are: Upper River, one on 24 Jan 1979 (A. Moore); Wallikunda, one on 28 Oct 1981; Diabugu, 4 on 28 Oct 1971 (GOS ABR 1981); Middle River, one on 11 Jan 1984; Kiang West, 2 on 23 Jun 1985 (both recorded amidst flocks of *A. affinis* (GOS RR)), doubtless stragglers from the known small breeding colony at Niokola Koba in Senegal.

262. APUS (=MICROPUS) PALLIDUS — PV, WV

Mouse-coloured (or Pallid) Swift

Rare passage but uncommon winter Palaearctic visitor, easily overlooked on passage amongst the large numbers of *A. apus*. Most records are for Dec–Jan. Maximum: 20 from Banjul Bund, 9 Feb 1966.

263. CHAETURA USSHERI — RB*

Ussher's Spine-tailed Swift (or Mottled-throated Spinetail)

Scarce resident (*C.u. ussheri*), locally distributed on the coast and inland along the river, particularly in Middle River. Present at Brufut throughout the year and undoubtedly breeds, but no nest has ever been found.

264. CYPSIURUS PARVUS — RB

Palm Swift

Locally common resident (*C.p. parvus*) on the coast and inland, always in the vicinity of palm trees, particularly *Borassus aethiopium*, in which it nests. May be under pressure as palms are being cut for building materials. The breeding season is extended, but most apparently nest during the rains, Jun–Oct.

COLIIDAE

265. COLIUS MACROURUS AV

Blue-naped Mousebird

African vagrant, only 2 records: party of six on the golf course at Fajara on 3 and 10 Jan 1975 (GOS ABR 1975) and a single at Tanji, 15 Nov 1986 (C. R. Barlow). Absence of other records is surprising as it is a not uncommon resident (*C.m. macrourus*) north of Kaolack in Senegal, 45 km from The Gambian border, and is reported also from Casamance (Bannerman 1930–51).

ALCEDINIDAE
Cerylinae

266. CERYLE (=MEGACERYLE) MAXIMA RB

Giant Kingfisher

Scarce resident on the coast and inland along the river; also occurs on narrow creeks and sometimes at small but usually deep, pools away from the river e.g. in Abuko Nature Reserve, where a pair is usually present. Breeds Oct–Feb; excavating nest-hole near Brikama, early Oct 1989 (C. R. Barlow, M. E. J. Gore).

267. CERYLE RUDIS RB

Pied Kingfisher

Common resident (*C.r. rudis*) on the coast and inland along the river. Breeding season is extended; at Fajara most adults were feeding young in holes on cliff-face Sep and Oct (GOS Rev, GOS ABR 1975). Cawkell gives breeding dates as Dec–Feb (Cawkell & Moreau).

Alcedininae

268. ALCEDO (=CORYTHORNIS) CRISTATA RB

Malachite Kingfisher

Not uncommon along creeks and waterways in Lower and Middle River. Most numerous during the rains, Jul–Oct, when it breeds; it is likely that dispersal away from The Gambia occurs during the dry season, though a few are present throughout the year.

269. ALCEDO QUADRIBRACHYS AfM

Shining-blue Kingfisher

Rare non-breeding intra-African migrant visitor (*A.q. quadribrachys*) in Lower and Middle River mostly during and immediately after the rains. First reported at Brumen Bridge in 1969 (no date given). Other records are: singles Brumen Bridge, Jan 1971 (GOS Rev), Jan 1977 (GOS ABR 1977); Abuko Nature Reserve, Jul–Aug 1974 (GOS Rev), 14 Dec 1975 (GOS ABR 1975), Oct–Nov 1977 (GOS ABR 1977), 18 Nov 1988 (J. N. Dymond); Georgetown, Jun 1986 (C. R. Barlow); Tendaba, Nov 1977 (GOS ABR 1977), 12 Dec 1984 and a pair 29 Dec 1985; Wallikunda, 8 Feb 1986; Kotu Stream, 22 Sep 1985 (GOS RR); 2 at Jakhaly, 24 Nov 1984 (Ericsson 1989). Regularly seen at Pirang Oct 1986 (G.G.F.R.).

270. CEYX (=ISPIDINA) PICTA RB, MB

Pigmy Kingfisher

A small resident population is augmented by wet season breeding visitors (*C.p. picta*), Jun–Nov. Uncommon but widely distributed in open bush and woodland throughout the country; occurs in gardens at Fajara. An insect feeder, often found far from water, though it will bathe by diving into a pool or stream without submerging. Breeds during the rains, Jul–Sep. Most disperse southwards after breeding.

Daceloninae

271. HALCYON CHELICUTI RB

Striped Kingfisher

Resident (*H.c. chelicuti*) and not uncommon in open woodland throughout the country. Insectivorous. Breeds Jun–Jul.

272. HALCYON LEUCOCEPHALA RB

Grey-headed Kingfisher

Not uncommon resident (*H.l. leucocephala*), most numerous in forest clearings in Middle and Upper River, but dispersal occurs after breeding and in some years numbers appear near the coast during the rains, Jul–Nov. Breeds at the end of the dry season, Apr-Jun.

273. HALCYON MALIMBICA RB

Blue-breasted Kingfisher

Uncommon resident (*h.m. torquata*). In the dry season is concentrated along the river, mostly in Middle and Upper River, and some in mangroves in Lower River. At the start of the rains, late Jun, they disperse away from the river to breed, normally excavating a nest-hole in arboreal termites nests. Pair excavating at Fajara, Jul 1976 (GOS ABR 1976) and Jul 1979 (GOS ABR 1979). Pair feeding young near Brikama, Sep–Oct 1989 (C. R. Barlow).

274. HALCYON SENEGALENSIS MB

Senegal (or Woodland) Kingfisher

Common breeding visitor in open country with scattered trees during and immediately after the rains, Jun–Dec. Breeds in holes in trees, Aug–Nov.

MEROPIDAE

275. MEROPS (=AEROPS) ALBICOLLIS AfM

White-throated Bee-eater

Irregular intra-African passage visitor, mostly seen on telegraph wires beside the road in Lower River, Nov–May. Movements are erratic: flocks of up to 40 appear intermittently throughout the dry season, first arriving in Nov; for a week or so they may be conspicuous, then disappearing for a month or more, only to reappear again. Most seen in Feb and Apr–May; also reported Jul–Aug.

276. MEROPS APIASTER PV, (WV)

European Bee-eater

Scarce Palaearctic passage visitor; flocks of 15–30 occur in open country annually Oct–Nov and Feb–Mar, but has been reported in all months Aug–Apr.

277. MEROPS (= MELITTOPHAGUS) BULOCKI WSV, (RB)

Red-throated Bee-eater

Mainly a not uncommon non-breeding visitor (*M.b. bulocki*), sometimes present in large flocks in Aug–Sep along Middle and Upper River. Breeding in The Gambia appears to be intermittant. There are large colonies along the upper reaches of the Gambia River in Senegal and there is clearly dispersal westwards into The Gambia from these during the off-season, from the end of the dry season and into the rains. Not recorded from Lower River. Breeding records: birds (no number given) observed entering 'pepper-pot' nesting holes in laterite cliff on north bank of river *c.* 10 miles upstream from Bansang, Jan 1962 (Cawkell 1965); active colony of 28 nest-holes in bank in Upper River, 19 Mar 1975 (Jensen & Kirkeby 1980); small colony in the river bank near Karantaba, 27 Oct 1981 (C. V. Eyre); in 1986 a substantial colony (50+ pairs) was located near Basse and has been occupied annually since (P. Byass); another small colony was found near Bansang in 1989 (R. Webzell).

278. MEROPS (= DICROCERCUS) HIRUNDINEUS RB

Swallow-tailed Bee-eater

Scare and local resident (*M.h. chrysolaimus*) in clearings in open woodland throughout the country. Breeds singly, though sometimes 2–3 pairs in fairly close proximity, immediately before and into the start of the rains, May-Jul.

279. MEROPS NUBICUS DSV, (RB)

Carmine Bee-eater

Common dry season visitor (*M.n. nubicus*) in open country in Middle and Upper River; scarce in Lower River and rare near the coast. Maximum *c.* 700 flying to roost near Jappeni, Jan 1972 (GOS Rev), but flocks up to 40 more usual. Several colonies reported in holes in high laterite banks along Middle and Upper River, Feb–Apr (no year given) (Bray *et al.*); 2 pairs apparently nesting in association with colony of *M. bulocki* near Karantaba, 27 Oct 1981 (C. V. Eyre) is the only recent breeding record.

280. MEROPS ORIENTALIS AfM

Little Green Bee-eater

A rare and occasional dry season visitor, late Oct–Jun, but several records in Upper River since 1987. Hopkinson reported that it occurred spasmodically, small parties being common for a few days at a time, Dec–Mar (Bannerman 1930–51). E. M. Cawkell saw it occasionally (latest date 21 Apr). Subsequent records are: Fajara, small flock (number not given), Feb 1968 (GOS Rev); Cape St Mary, one on 28 Oct 1977 (Jenson & Kirkeby 1980); Bansang, 2 on 23–26 Apr 1980 (GOS ABR 1980); several independent substantiated records in Upper River 1987–89; Kuntaur, one on 11 Feb and 2 on 15 Feb–early Mar 1988 (P. Donnelly & B. Macdonald).

Probably occurred Tendeba, 18 Nov 1985 and Kerewan, 28 Dec 1985 but identification uncertain (GOS R).

281. MEROPS (=MELITTOPHAGUS) PUSILLUS RB

Little Bee-eater

Common resident (*M.p. pusillus*) in open country with scattered low bushes and open scrub; most numerous in Lower River, scarce up-country. Breeds singly Apr–Jul, excavating nest-hole in a low bank.

282. MEROPS SUPERCILIOSUS (=PERSICUS) PV, WV

Blue-cheeked (or Madagascar) Bee-eater

Common visitor, particularly in Lower River, Oct–Apr, usually in the vicinity of water; sometimes abundant in mangrove near Banjul during migration in Nov and Mar when flocks of 50–100 occur, but has been recorded in all months of the year. Assumed to be *M.s. chrysocercus*, which breeds in North Africa.

CORACIIDAE

283. CORACIAS ABYSSINICA DSV, RB

Abyssinian Roller

Common dry season visitor in open country with scattered trees, Nov–Apr; probably the most conspicuous bird at this season. Up to 20 often gather at a bushfire to hawk for insects. Hopkinson stated that breeding starts about 1 May (Bannerman 1930–51). A few pairs appear to breed annually; display flighting observed at Keneba, 3 July 1977 (GOS ABR 1977); a pair feeding young in a hole in a dead palm tree near Marakissa, 28 June–7 Jul 1980 (GOS ABR 1980); recently fledged young at Fajara annually 1987–89 (C. White). Clearly most leave shortly before the beginning of the rains to breed elsewhere, presumably in the drier northern areas, and some non-breeding birds remain throughout the rains; there is evidence of southward migration after breeding, Aug–Sep (M. E. Smalley, *Malimbus* 5:34–36, 1983).

284. CORACIAS CYANOGASTER RB

Blue-bellied Roller

Common resident, widely distributed in clearings with scattered trees and on the borders of open forest throughout the country. Breeding recorded May–Jul.

285. CORACIAS GARRULUS ?PV, ?WV

European Roller

Status uncertain; it is usually not possible to separate in the field the immatures of this Palaearctic species and *C. abyssinica*. Probably a scarce passage and winter visitor with the occasional non-breeding bird over-summering. Smalley (*Malimbus* 5:34, 1983) positively identified 7 during a study at Fajara, 1977–81: singles, 13 and 23 June 1978 (probably the same bird), 15 and 18 Feb 1979 (probably the same bird), 1 Mar, 12 and 14 May, 13 June 1979, and 26 Nov 1980. Other records are Banjul, Jan 1968 (Morel 1972); Cape Rd, 25 Jan 1983 (GOS RR); Jakhaly, 10 Feb 1987 (GOS ABR 1986–87).

286. CORACIAS NAEVIA RB*

Rufous-crowned Roller

Resident (*C.n. naevia*), widely distributed in open bush and cleared land with scattered trees, throughout the country, but nowhere common. Almost certainly breeds: a pair at Mansakonko in Jan 1966 behaved as if nesting (Bray *et al.*), but no nest has ever been found.

287. EURYSTOMUS GLAUCURUS (=AFER) RB

Broad-billed Roller

Common resident (*E.g. afer*), usually in the vicinity of water; most numerous in Middle and Upper River. In non-breeding season flocks of several hundred (max *c.* 500, Upper River end Nov-early Dec 1981 (GOS ABR 1981)) gather and hawk for insects over the river and at bush fires. Dispersal occurs before the start of the rains, May–Jun, when breeding begins.

[EURYSTOMUS GULARIS Rejected

Blue-throated Roller

The one (1975) record in GOSREV is not acceptable and the species is deleted from The Gambia list.]

UPUPIDAE

288. UPUPA EPOPS RB, WV?

Hoopoe

A scarce resident and probably a not uncommon migrant from the Palaearctic. It is difficult to separate in the field the resident race, *U.e. senegalensis*, from the migrant European nominate race, and all specimens collected to date have been *senegalensis*. Occurs in open woodland and is generally scarce, though numbers appear to increase Dec–Feb which suggests that the local population is augmented by migrants from Europe and the Mediterranean. The resident race breeds Mar–Apr.

PHOENICULIDAE

289. PHOENICULUS (=SCOPTELUS) ATERRIMUS RB

Lesser (or Black) Wood-Hoopoe

Scarce resident (*P.a. aterrimus*), widely but locally distributed in woodland throughout the country. Numbers appear to be decreasing, doubtless due to the disappearance of forest. Breeding first proved in 1989 when pair observed feeding a newly fledged youngster at Yundum (C. R. Barlow).

290. PHOENICULUS PURPUREUS (=ERYTHRORHYNCHUS) RB

Senegal (or Green) Wood-Hoopoe

Common resident (*P.p. senegalensis*), widely distributed in open country with scattered trees, often in the vicinity of towns and villages. Breeds during the rains, Jun–Nov; co-operative nesters (C. R. Barlow).

BUCEROTIDAE

291. BUCORVUS ABYSSINICUS — RB

(Abyssinian) Ground Hornbill

Uncommon resident in cleared agricultural land and open bush with scattered large trees throughout the country. Breeds during and just after the rains, Sep–Jan; 2 family parties, with 3 and 4 fledged juveniles, were seen on the north bank between Kuntaur and Farafenni, 7 Feb 1978 (M. E. J. Gore) and a pair feeding young in hollow rhun palm *Borassus aethiopium* stump, 10 Oct 1979 (GOS ABR 1979). Recent indications are that numbers are decreasing.

[BYCANISTES SUBCYLINDRICUS — Rejected

Black-and-White Casqued Hornbill

The only record, of one in Banjul town, Mar 1969 (Jensen & Kirkeby 1980), must be considered to have been an escape from a visiting ship. Not known to occur north of Ivory Coast; Ghanaian vessels call regularly at Banjul and were present in the harbour when the bird was seen.]

292. TOCKUS (=LOPHOCEROS) ERYTHRORHYNCHUS — RB

Red-beaked (or Red-billed) Hornbill

Resident and common (*T.e. erythrorhynchus*) in open bush and agricultural land with scattered trees and in gardens throughout the country, but probably most numerous in Middle and Upper River. Feeding young at Fajara in Dec.

293. TOCKUS FASCIATUS (=LOPHOCEROS SEMIFASCIATUS) — RB

Black-and-White-tailed (or Allied) Hornbill

Local but not uncommon resident (*T.f. semifasciatus*) in remaining high forest on the south bank in Lower River inland of the coast to Km 140, where pairs and small parties are seen in all months. Maximum of 22 observed going to roost near Abuko, Jan 1975 (M. E. J. Gore). No records from elsewhere. Nesting recorded in Abuko in Aug.

294. TOCKUS (=LOPHOCEROS) NASUTUS — RB

Grey Hornbill

Common resident (*T.n. nasutus*), widely distributed in open woodland and open country with scattered trees, throughout the country. Breeds after the rains, Nov–Mar. After nesting, flocks up to 20 may be seen and local movements occur, particularly during the early part of the rains, Jul–Aug; these movements, not fully understood, are presumably governed by the fruiting of different species of trees.

CAPITONIDAE

295. LYBIUS (=POGONORNIS) DUBIUS — RB

Bearded Barbet

Common resident in open country where there are scattered trees; also on the edge of open woodland. Breeds May–Aug; feeding young in nest-hole on the main trunk of a dead tree, just beneath the base of a branch, at Yundum and Fajara, Jun and Jul 1976 respectively and nested in hole in rhun palm at Fajara, Aug 1977.

Marshes and ricefields are an important habitat, particularly during the dry season when much of the surrounding area dries up. Above: a Hammerkop *Scopus umbretta* is pictured with an African bull-frog. Below: a female Painted Snipe *Rostratula benghalensis,* one of the few bird species in which the female is brighter than the male and the male alone incubates the eggs.

Two birds found mainly up-river, though both may sometimes be seen near the coast particularly at Abuko Nature Reserve: Hadada *Bostrychia hagedash* (above), whose call is one of the most familiar sounds along Middle River, and an African Darter *Anhinga rufa,* also known as the Snake Bird because of its habit of swimming almost submerged with only its neck and head above water.

The White-faced Scops Owl *Otus leucotis* (above) is resident and not uncommon in open woodland while the Red-billed Wood-Dove *Turtur afer* also occurs in gardens.

The Standard-wing Nightjar *Macrodipteryx longipennis* (a male is shown above in breeding plumage) and Four-banded Sand-grouse *Pterocles quadricinctus* are birds of the savanna. Both occur on cleared land near the coast.

Two of the brightest coloured and most noticeable birds which are found in open country at different times of the year: the Abyssinian Roller *Coracias abyssinica* (above) is mainly a dry season visitor, while the male Red Bishop *Euplectes orix* is in colour during the rains – for the rest of the year he is drab brown-streaked.

Two birds of open woodland: Bearded Barbet *Lybius dubius* (above) and Grey Woodpecker *Mesopicos goertae*. Both also occur in larger gardens at Fajara where these were photographed at their nestholes.

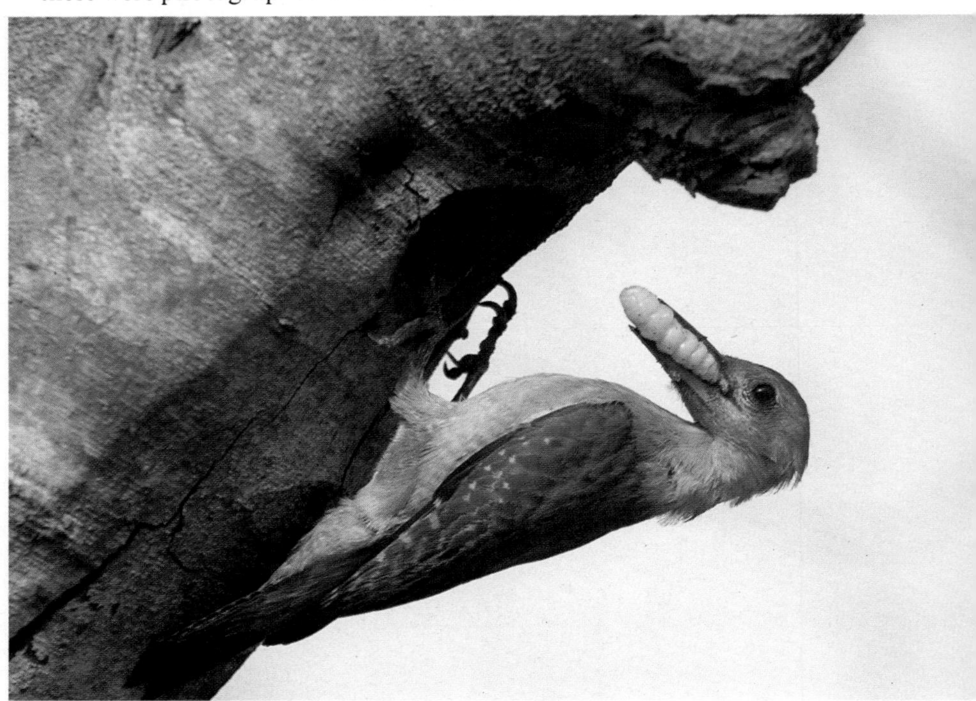

The tiny Yellow-fronted Barbet (or Tinkerbird) *Pogoniulus chrysoconus* (above) and Grey Hornbill *Tockus nasutus* are found in similar habitat.

Common garden birds: a pair of Yellow-fronted Canaries *Serinus mozambicus* (above) at their nest and a Long-tailed Shrike *Corvinella corvina*.

Barbary Shrike (or Gonolek) *Laniarius barbarus* (above) and White-crowned Robin-Chat *Cossypha albicapilla,* both photographed at their nests in gardens at Fajara.

The open bush and fallow land at Brufut is a particularly rich habitat. A male Little Bee-eater *Merops pusillus* (above) is pictured presenting a bee to his mate while a Black-crowned Tchagra *Tchagra senegala* was photographed at its nest nearby.

The spectacular Carmine Bee-eater *Merops nubicus* occurs in open country up-river.

Two birds which are closely connected with human habitation: Wire-tailed Swallows *Hirundo smithii* (above) will sometimes nest on a verandah while the Speckled Pigeon *Columba guinea* often nests under the eaves of houses.

The Black Magpie (or Piapiac) *Ptilostomus afer* (above) and Yellow-billed Oxpecker *Buphagus africanus* are found in the vicinity of villages as they usually accompany livestock, the former catching insects disturbed by the animals, the latter taking ticks off the animals themselves.

Seven typical weavers occur in The Gambia: Little Weaver *Ploceus luteolus* (above) and Vitelline Masked Weaver *Ploceus velatus*.

Village Weaver *Ploceus cucullatus* (above) and Black-headed Weaver *Ploceus melanocephalus*.

More often heard than seen the Grey-backed Camaroptera *Camaroptera brachyura*, pictured here at its nest which is sewn into the leaves of a low bush, is widely distributed in open woodland and gardens throughout the country.

296. LYBIUS VIEILLOTI RB

Vieillot's Barbet

Uncommon resident (*L.v. rubescens*), locally but widely distributed on the edge of open woodland and cultivated land with scattered trees. Recorded from Barra, Brufut, Tanji, Yundum, Keneba, Tendaba, Mansakonko and Sami. Breeding recorded May-Jul.

297. POGONIULUS BILINEATUS (=LEUCOLAIMA) RB

Lemon-rumped Tinker-bird

Scarce resident (*P.b. sharpei*) in woodland, apparently confined to Lower River. Seen and heard regularly at Fajara, Brufut and Abuko Nature Reserve. Breeding first confirmed at Brufut, 30 Jun 1980 (GOS ABR 1980).

298. POGONIULUS CHRYSOCONUS RB

Yellow-fronted Barbet (or Tinker-bird)

Resident (*P.c. chrysoconus*) and common throughout the country, its call being one of the most familiar sounds in open woodland. Breeding season is extended: most nest May–Aug, but young were being fed in nest-hole at Fajara, Dec 1977.

INDICATORIDAE

299. INDICATOR INDICATOR RB

Black-throated Honey-Guide

The most widespread of the 3 honey-guide species, not uncommon in open bush with scattered trees and woodland in Lower and Middle River; few records from Upper River, but probably as common. Parasitic; only breeding record is 2 young being fed by 2 pairs of *Merops pusillus*, 25–26 Jul 1964 (G. & P. Gore *per* E. M. Cawkell).

300. INDICATOR MACULATUS RB*

Spotted Honey-Guide

Rare resident (*I.m. maculatus*), apparently confined to the few remaining areas of dense forest in Lower River and in riverine forest further inland. Bannerman (1930–51) refers to one in the British Museum labelled 'Gambia river'. Regularly reported in Abuko Nature Reserve but few records from elsewhere: singles Baboon I., 2 Mar 1975 (GOS Rev); Brufut, (trapped and photographed), 26 Mar 1975 (GOS ABR 1975); Fajara, 31 Mar 1976 (GOS ABR 1976) and 10 Nov 1979 (GOS ABR 1979); Brikama, Jun 1989 and Yundum, Aug 1989 (C. R. Barlow). Parasitic, breeding dates unknown.

301. INDICATOR MINOR RB

Lesser Honey-Guide

Recorded (*I.m. senegalensis*) only from Lower River, where it is an uncommon resident in open woodland and gardens; regularly seen at Abuko Nature Reserve, Fajara, Brufut, Yundum and Kiang West. No records from further inland. Breeds (parasitically) May–Jun; has been seen attempting to enter nest-hole of *Lybius vieilloti*.

PICIDAE
Jynginae

302. JYNX TORQUILLA PV, WV

European Wryneck

Scarce Palaearctic passage and winter visitor (*J.t. torquilla*) in open bush. Recorded 11 Sep–4 Apr, most Nov–Jan. Until recently all records were from Lower River, but probably overlooked inland: single at Jakhaly, 24 Nov 1984 (Ericcson 1989).

Picinae

303. CAMPETHERA ABINGONI RB

Golden-tailed Woodpecker

Lowe collected this species in The Gambia (Bannerman 1930–51), but it is rare. All but one of the records, all singles, are from Lower River: Brufut, Jul 1973; Kalaji, Nov 1973; Fajara, Feb 1975; Tanji, Apr 1975 (GOS Rev), 3 Jan 1989 and 20 May 1989 (C. R. Barlow); Banjul, 27 Feb 1983; Abuko, 8 Dec 1983, 14 Jan 1984; km 60, 11 Feb 1984. The inland record is of one at Basse, 22 Nov 1984 (GOS RR). Evidence of breeding is female seen to feed a juvenile at Camaloo, 16 June 1964 (G. & P. Gore *per* E. M. Cawkell).

304. CAMPETHERA NIVOSA RB*

Buff-spotted Woodpecker

Rare resident (*C.n. nivosa*) in forest in Lower River. First recorded 19 Jul 1963, when one flew into a house at Fajara and was identified in the hand (Cawkell 1965); another there in May 1984 (GOS RR). Most other records are of individuals and pairs in Abuko Nature Reserve where it has been reported throughout the year and almost certainly breeds, but there is no evidence. A few pairs are also probably resident, but overlooked, in the other remaining areas of forest in Lower River. One at Fajara, May 1985 (GOS RR); a pair at Pirang twice in May 1985 and once in Oct 1986 (G.G.F.P.).

305. CAMPETHERA PUNCTULIGERA RB

Fine-spotted Woodpecker

The commonest woodpecker, resident (*C.p. punctuligera*) and widely distributed in woodland throughout the country. Breeding recorded Jul–Aug.

306. DENDROCOPOS (=DENDROPICOS) OBSOLETUS RB

Lesser White-spotted (or Brown-backed) Woodpecker

Scarce resident (*D.o. obsoletus*) in open woodland, widely distributed throughout the country; recorded from the coast to east of Basse. Breeding suspected at Brufut in Mar; immature seen at Yundum in Jun.

307. DENDROPICOS ELACHUS ?

Least (or Little) Grey Woodpecker

An arid savanna species which is possibly resident, but overlooked. Only 4 records: Bwiam, 3 on 10 Jun 1956; Brufut, one in Aug 1959 (Cawkell 1965);

Georgetown, a pair on 30 Dec 1974 (Jensen & Kirkeby 1980); Farafenni, a pair on 6 May 1986 (GOS RR).

308. DENDROPICOS FUSCESCENS RB

Cardinal Woodpecker

Scarce resident (*D.f. lafresnayi*), widely distributed but local, on the edge of open woodland and in clearings with scattered trees. Recorded from Fajara, Brufut (where it is seen regularly throughout the year), Yundum, Tendaba, Keneba and Sapu. Excavating nest-hole at Brufut, 27 Jul 1976 (GOS ABR 1976) and feeding young there, Jul 1977 (GOS ABR 1977).

309. MESOPICOS GOERTAE RB

Grey Woodpecker

Resident (*M.g. goertae*) and common in open woodland. Breeds during the latter part of the dry season, Mar–May. Observed copulating 28 Apr 1964, and quarrelling with *Phoeniculus purpureus* at hole in palm tree, 16 May 1964 (Bray *et al.*). Feeding young in nest at Barra, Apr 1977 (GOS ABR 1977) and nearly full-grown young in nest at Fajara, early Apr 1978 (M. E. J. Gore).

PASSERIFORMES

ALAUDIDAE

[CALANDRELLA BRACHYDACTYLA Rejected

Short-toed Lark

The 2 records (1973 and 1975) in Jensen & Kirkeby (1980) are not acceptable.]

310. EREMOPTERIX LEUCOTIS RB*

Chestnut-backed Finch-Lark (or Sparrow-Lark)

Locally resident and not uncommon (*E.l. melanocephala*) in dry open country and grassland on the north bank in Middle and Upper River. Scarce on the south bank, though regularly at Soma and near the airport at Yundum, where breeding was suspected, but not proved, Feb 1976 (M. E. J. Gore). Occasionally occurs on the coast. Breeding unrecorded.

[EREMOPTERIX NIGRICEPS

White-fronted Finch-Lark

The record of a pair at Yundum, Jan 1976 (Jensen & Kirkeby 1980) was not accepted by the GOS and requires confirmation.]

311. GALERIDA CRISTATA RB

Crested Lark

Confined to the littoral (*G.c. senegallensis*) where it is locally common. Resident along Banjul Bund, Mile 3, Camaloo, Kotu Beach and Tanji; probably also along the coast to the Casamance border and on the coast on the north bank of the river, although there are no records. Breeding season extended, Nov–May, most Dec–Feb. One seen in Middle River, 22 Mar 1975 (Jensen & Kirkeby 1980) was probably a vagrant from the Palaearctic.

312. MIRAFRA CANTILLANS AV

Singing Bush Lark

African vagrant, only one record: a single bird (photographed and sketched, with a full description) at Keneba, 4 Dec 1986 present for several days and seen by two observers (GOS ABR 1986–87). In West Africa occurs locally in arid country from Mauritania and Senegal south to Nigeria and Cameroon (Serle *et al.* 1977).

313. MIRAFRA NIGRICANS (=PINAROCORYS ERYTHROPYGIA) AV

Rufous-rumped (or Red-tailed) Bush-Lark

African vagrant; the only records are of a single bird, almost certainly the same one, near Banjul on 31 Dec 1960 and on 1 and 8 Jan 1961 (Cawkell & Moreau).

314. MIRAFRA RUFOCINNAMOMEA (=BUCKLEYI) RB?

Flappet Lark

Rare (*M.r. buckleyi*), but widely distributed and presumably resident. Largest flocks: 12, seen on several occasions, Feb 1962 (Cawkell & Moreau) and 5 near Basse, 26 Nov 1984 (Ericsson 1989). Other records, all singles, are: Banjul Bund, 28 Jun 1966 (Bray *et al.*); Farafenni, 24 Jul 1973 (GOS Rev); Bansang, 11 Oct 1978 (P. Goll). No evidence of breeding.

HIRUNDINIDAE

315. DELICHON URBICA PV, WV

European House Martin

Uncommon Palaearctic and winter visitor (*D.u. urbica*), usually seen in flocks over the river but numbers are variable each year. Most numerous on northward migration, Mar–May (latest 6 Jun), when flocks of over 100 may be encountered anywhere. Flocks recorded along Middle and Upper River (only occasionally in Lower River), Nov–Jan; maximum 250+ near Bansang, 3 Dec 1965 (GOS Rev).

316. HIRUNDO ABYSSINICA AV

Lesser Striped Swallow

Rare African vagrant, only 2 records: 4 (*H.a. puella*) between Basse and Fatoto, 30 May 1969 (Morel 1972); one with a large flock of *H. rustica* at Fajara, 16 May 1980 (GOS ABR 1980). A savanna bird recorded in Senegal east of the Gambia at Niokola Koba.

317. HIRUNDO DAURICA (=RUFULA) RB

Red-rumped Swallow

Locally common resident (*H.d. domicella*) inland in villages and townships; rare on the coast. Most breed Feb–May but season sometimes extends into the rains, Sep–Oct, under bridges, eaves, etc.

[HIRUNDO FULIGULA (=PTYONOPROGNE RUFIGULA)

African Rock Martin

One unconfirmed record only: a single (*H.f. rufigula?*) at Kaur, Jan 1972 (Jensen & Kirkeby 1980). A mainly East African species which ranges west to Mali, Nigeria, Ghana and Ivory Coast. In view of the difficulty in separating the several small dark African hirundines I have placed it in square brackets.]

318. HIRUNDO (=PSEUDOHIRUNDO) GRISEOPYGA AV

Grey-rumped Swallow

Rare African vagrant, only 2 records: Fatoto, 2 on 12 Jan 1957 (Cawkell 1960); Kotu Stream, *c.* 10 among a large hirundine movement, 27 Dec 1980 (GOS ABR 1980). Moreau saw 6 swallows which were probably this species at Basse, 6 Jan 1961 (Cawkell & Moreau).

319. HIRUNDO LEUCOSOMA RB*

Pied-winged Swallow

Local resident, widely distributed but nowhere common, usually in the vicinity of water, sometimes in forest clearings. Recorded from Banjul, Fajara, Abuko, Kabafitta, Mansakonko, Bansang and Fatoto. Believed to breed Apr–Jun; seen entering and leaving a hollow Baobab tree at Mansakonko, 15 Jun 1973 (GOS Rev) and probably nesting, but breeding not yet proved.

320. HIRUNDO LUCIDA RB

Red-chested Swallow

Abundant resident, breeding under eaves, in most towns and villages, Mar–May. (Previously considered a sub-species of *H. rustica* and treated as such in the 1st Edition but now generally accepted as being a distinct species.)

321. HIRUNDO RUSTICA PV

European Swallow

Common Palaearctic passage migrant, usually in small flocks up to 25, 4 Oct–12 Nov and 14 Mar–4 May. Maximum together, 150–200 feeding on a hatch of insects over Sapu ricefields, 2 May 1976 (GOS ABR 1976).

322. HIRUNDO SEMIRUFA RB*

Rufous-breasted (or -chested) Swallow

Rare and local resident (*H.s. gordoni*) in open country, usually in the vicinity of villages. Recorded only from Kotu Stream, Abuko, Pirang, Keneba and Pakali Ba. Has been seen in most months and almost certainly breeds, but there are no records.

323. HIRUNDO SENEGALENSIS MB, RB

Mosque Swallow

Common (*H.s. senegalensis*) when breeding before and during the rains, May–Oct; dispersal then occurs, most presumably moving south to wetter areas, though some remain along the river. Recorded in all months. Several flocks of 10–16 birds along Middle River, 8 Mar 1976 (GOS ABR 1976). Breeding in hollow Baobab tree near Cape St Mary in Jul and in roof of building at Yoroberikunda in Aug.

324. HIRUNDO SMITHII — RB

Wire-tailed Swallow

Resident (*H.s. smithii*), and common on the coast and Lower River numbers having increased noticeably in the past 10 years. Rare further inland; recorded near Basse in Nov (Ericsson 1989) and Fatoto in Jan (GOS Rev). Bannerman (1930–51) states that the species does not occur as far west as The Gambia; discounting a 'reference in old literature' as 'doubtless incorrect'. He was apparently unaware of a specimen collected at a nest, C/3, at Bathurst (now Banjul) (Rendall 1892) and extant in the Liverpool Museum. Not recorded in this century until *c.* 6 were seen near Gunjur, 11 Feb 1962 (Landsborough Thomson, *Ibis* 108: 292), since when reported regularly. Being local it was presumably overlooked by Hopkinson, but it may have increased on account of concrete buildings, e.g. houses and bridges, providing new nesting sites. Usually in the vicinity of water but not invariably so, and often breeds away from water. Breeds throughout the year, with apparent peaks Jan–Mar and Jul–Aug. This concurs with Malawi and Zimbabwe records, where double peak breeding occurs, i.e. in both wet and dry seasons (Benson & Benson 1977). Breeding recorded under bridges, in derelict buildings, once in occupied room of a house and on a verandah, both at Yundum. C/3 usual.

325. PSALIDOPROCNE OBSCURA — DSV, RB?

Fanti (or Fantee) Rough-winged Swallow

A species which has extended its range into The Gambia in recent years. An adult male was first recorded in Lower River, 14 Jun 1969 (Morel 1972). During the 1970s there were several more records, most in forest clearings, and there were also a number of records of small, dusky black swallows which were tentatively identified as *P. fuliginosa*. An examination of skins at the BMNH in comparison with a photograph (M. E. J. Gore) of one of these swallows clearly showed them to be immature, probably female *P. obscura*. Records have increased since 1980 with regular sightings at Abuko Nature Reserve (max *c.* 30 on 1 Apr 1981) and elsewhere and it is clearly now a regular, mainly dry season, visitor and possibly a local resident, as there are records for all months and immatures have been seen, but breeding has not been proved. *P. fuliginosa* has been deleted from The Gambia list.

326. RIPARIA CINCTA — AV, FB?

Banded Martin

Today a rare African vagrant. Bannerman (1930–51) refers to a sand martin which he believed to be *R.c. cincta* and which was 'common all the year round' adding that Hopkinson saw plenty of their holes in the banks along Upper River. Cawkell (1965) states that they certainly no longer breed and cites only one record: a single bird in Middle River, Jan 1963. Only 2 records since: a single bird over the river at Sapu, 9 Apr 1975 (GOS ABR 1975) and one amidst a large flock of *Hirundo rustica* at Fajara, 16 May 1980 (GOS ABR 1980).

327. RIPARIA PALUDICOLA — AV

African Sand Martin

African vagrant, only 7 records: Camaloo, one on 14 Jan 1972; Lower River, 2 on 29 Jan 1974, 5 on 12 Jan 1975; Keneba, 10 on 21 Nov 1977 (Jensen & Kirkeby

1980); Pirang, 2 with other hirundines on 25 Nov 1986 (J. N. Dymond); Tendaba, 6 on 22 Nov 1984 (Ericsson 1989), *c.* 20 on 25 Nov and *c.* 30 on 30 Nov 1988 (J. N. Dymond). Locally distributed in the savanna from Senegal to Chad.

328. RIPARIA RIPARIA PV, WV

European Sand Martin

Common Palaearctic passage and winter visitor (*R.r. riparia*) along Middle River, probably also Upper River but there are few records; rarely seen in Lower River. Large numbers pass through in Mar; maximum reported, several thousand between Sapu and Kaur, 7 Mar 1976 (GOS ABR 1976). Fewer occur on southward passage, Sep–Nov.

MOTACILLIDAE

329. ANTHUS CAMPESTRIS (WV)

Tawny Pipit

Rare Palaearctic winter visitor on open ground. All records Dec–Mar, possibly largely overlooked. Moreau saw 2 on the edge of the salt flats at Keneba, Dec 1960 and Cawkell saw it twice on the littoral in Jan and Mar (no year given) (Cawkell & Moreau). Recent records, all singles, are: Yundum, 18 Jan 1963 (G. and P. Gore), 20 Jan 1976; Camaloo, 18 Dec 1976 (GOS ABR 1976), 20 Nov 1986 (GOS ABR 1986–87); Pirang, 25 Nov 1986; Soma, 26 Nov 1986; Barra, 19 Nov 1988 (J. N. Dymond).

330. ANTHUS CERVINUS PV, WV

Red-throated Pipit

Scarce but regular Palaearctic passage and winter visitor. First recorded 8 Apr 1962 (Cawkell & Moreau). Since then parties of up to 12 observed several times on open ground near water at Camaloo, Banjul Bund and Yellitenda, Nov–May, most in Apr.

[ANTHUS HODGSONI

Olive-backed Pipit

This species was accepted (GOS RR) as a vagrant to The Gambia on the basis of a full description of a single bird near the Sunwing Hotel, Cape St Mary, Dec 1984. *A. hodgsoni* breeds in eastern Asia and winters in south-east Asia. It occurs fairly frequently as a vagrant in western Europe, including Britain, and it is possible that one might continue southwards to West Africa on the same latitude as its wintering grounds in Asia. Notwithstanding, the record must be considered as questionable because *A. hodgsoni* can be confused with *A. trivialis* which sometimes shows a dark patch on the rear of the ear-coverts and as it is so far out of its normal range.]

331. ANTHUS LEUCOPHRYS RB

Plain-backed Pipit

Resident (*A.l. ansorgei*), widely distributed in open short grass country, usually near water, but nowhere common. Recorded at Camaloo, Cape St Mary, Kotu Stream, Yundum, Keneba, Bwiam, Mansakonko and Sapu. Breeds Apr–Jul, nest C/2 at Yundum 19 Apr, fledglings at Camaloo, 30 May at Bwiam, 8 Jun and near Brikama, Jul.

332. ANTHUS TRIVIALIS PV, WV

Tree Pipit

Mainly a scarce Palaearctic passage visitor (*A.t. trivialis*) in open country with scattered trees, near the coast, Sep–Dec and Mar–May; a few over-winter. Maximum recorded *c.* 12 in Banjul garden, 7–8 Mar 1966; *c.* 6 Keneba, 9 Mar 1975 (GOS Rev); 4–5 present at Fajara, 3–19 May 1979 (GOS ABR 1979) is a late record.

333. MACRONYX CROCEUS RB

Yellow-throated Long-claw

Resident and widely distributed on the borders of freshwater swamps throughout the country, but nowhere common. Recorded from Camaloo, Abuko, Bwiam, Mansakonko, Jappeni, Sapu, Jakhaly, Berending and Fatoto. Breeding recorded Jun–Aug.

334. MOTACILLA AGUIMP AV

African Pied Wagtail

African vagrant, only 2 records: reported by Morel from The Gambia (location not given), 30 May 1969 (Morel 1972); 2 at Fatoto, 16 Dec 1973 (Jensen & Kirkeby 1980). It occurs regularly along the Gambia River about 140 kms upstream in Niokola Koba National Park in Senegal. One reported at Bakau, 23 Dec 1982 is probable but was not accepted because insufficient details were supplied (GOS RR).

335. MOTACILLA ALBA WV

White Wagtail

Common Palaearctic winter visitor, 15 Sep–16 Apr. Most arrive Oct and is then widespread until Mar on open ground, usually, but not invariably, in the vicinity of water. Most numerous near the coast but occurs throughout the country.

[MOTACILLA CINEREA

Grey Wagtail

No confirmed records despite inclusion in previous publications. Both Rendall (1892) and Hopkinson (Bannerman 1930–51) describe it without evidence as a rare winter visitor, the latter merely referring to one identified 'almost for certain' at Kudang, 14 Mar 1907. Other unconfirmed sightings, all singles, are Banjul, 18 and 19 May 1964 (Bray *et al.*); 10 Nov 1985 (GOS RR).]

336. MOTACILLA FLAVA PV, WV

Yellow (or Blue-headed) Wagtail

Three races of *M. flava* occur on open ground, usually near water but not invariably so, e.g. on sports fields, including MacCarthy Square in the centre of Banjul. Most numerous, and then generally common, on passage from the Palaearctic, Sep–Nov and Feb–Apr; main passage Oct and Mar, when they may be abundant for a few days in flocks of several hundred. Only a few over-winter. Mostly *flava* with *flavissima* and *thunbergi* occurring in smaller numbers. It is likely that *cinereocapilla* and *iberiae* also occur but have been unrecognised.

CAMPEPHAGIDAE

337. CAMPEPHAGA PHOENICEA RB

Red-shouldered Cuckoo-Shrike

Rare resident (*C.p. phoenicae*), widely distributed in remaining forest throughout the country. Seen carrying nesting material in Aug is evidence of breeding early in the rains. Bannerman (1930–51) suggests it is partially migratory in The Gambia, but there is no recent evidence to confirm this.

338. CORACINA PECTORALIS RB

White-breasted Cuckoo-Shrike

Rare and local resident in remaining high forest; all records except one are from Lower River. Hopkinson (1919) regarded it as a 'rare visitor to The Gambia in the rains'. However, recently it has been seen regularly and throughout the year at Kabafitta Forest Reserve. Other records from Yundum, Jambur, Tendaba, and Farababantang. Once recorded at Mansakonko. Only breeding record is June, C/2 (Cawkell & Moreau).

PYCNONOTIDAE

339. ANDROPADUS VIRENS RB*

Little Green Bulbul (or Greenbul)

Resident (*A.v. erythropterus*) and locally common in remaining dense woodland; regularly seen or heard in Abuko Nature Reserve, where it is present throughout the year. Also recorded recently from Fajara, Brufut, Jambur, Howbah and Sukuta. No records from further inland. Almost certainly breeds but no nest has ever been found.

340. BLEDA CANICAPILLA RB*

Grey-headed Bristle-bill

Rare and local resident in remnant forest. Bannerman (1930–51) refers to it occurring in The Gambia; recorded at Cape St Mary on several occasions in the 1970s, but all recent records are from Abuko Nature Reserve, with maximum 4 on 2 Jan 1976 (GOS ABR 1975–76) and 3 on 26 Feb 1983 (GOS RR) and Pirang where it was seen in May 1985 and 2 were trapped, Oct 1986 (G.G.F.P.). Almost certainly breeds, but there is no evidence.

341. CHLOROCICHLA (=PYRRHURUS) FLAVICOLLIS RB

Yellow-throated Leaf-love

Resident (*C.f. flavicollis*) and locally common in thick bush and riverine forest. Formerly thought to be confined to Lower and Middle River but there are recent records from Bansang and Basse and it, therefore, appears to be distributed in suitable habitat throughout the country. Breeds Jul–Sep.

[CRINIGER (=TRICHOPHORUS) OLIVACEUS Deleted

Yellow-throated Olive Greenbul

The type specimen obtained in 1837 is labelled 'Gambia'. Bannerman (1930–51), however, doubted that it occurred in The Gambia but said that specimens had been obtained in Casamance, Senegal. Serle *et al.* (1977) give its range as Senegal to Ghana but as there are no records this century it is deleted from The Gambia list.]

342. NICATOR CHLORIS ?

West African Nicator

Status uncertain, possibly a rare and local resident (*N.c. chloris*) in little remaining high forest in Lower River. Recorded only from Abuko Nature Reserve: one early Feb 1974 (GOS Rev), 2–3 on 12 and 23 Dec 1975 (GOS ABR 1975), and 2 on 16 Nov 1984 (Ericsson 1989). No records since.

343. PHYLLASTREPHUS (=PYRRHURUS) SCANDENS RB*

Leaf-love

Scarce resident (*P.s. scandens*) in riverine forest; also in thick bush away from water. Cawkell (1965) associated it with the palm *Phoenix reclinata*. Recent records from Abuko, Fajara, Howbah and Sukutu. Certainly breeds, but no nest has ever been found.

344. PYCNONOTUS BARBATUS RB

Common Garden (or White-vented) Bulbul

Abundant resident (*P.b. inornatus*) in open bush and in gardens throughout the country; probably the best-known bird in The Gambia because of its distinctive song. Breeds Jun–Oct, C/3 usual.

345. THESCELOCICHLA LEUCOPLEURUS AV

Swamp Palm Bulbul (or White-tailed Greenbul)

African vagrant, recorded twice during the rains: a single bird was seen in Abuko Nature Reserve, 29 Oct 1968 (GOS Rev) and one (or more) were heard singing regularly in swamp forest at Pirang, Oct 1986 (G.G.F.P.).

LANIIDAE
Prionopinae

346. PRIONOPS PLUMATA RB

Long- (or straight-) crested Helmet-Shrike

Uncommon resident (*P.p. plumata*) widely distributed in woodland, occurring in parties up to 20. Breeding season is extended, May–Oct.

Malaconotinae

347. DRYOSCOPUS GAMBENSIS RB

Gambian Puff-back Shrike (or Puff-back)

Not uncommon resident (*D.g. gambensis*) in open forest, also in larger gardens; occurs throughout the country but appears to be more numerous near the coast. Breeds Jun–Oct. The emblem of The Gambia Ornithological Society.

348. LANIARIUS BARBARUS RB

Barbary Shrike (or Gonolek)

Common resident (*L.b. barbarus*), widely distributed in dense bush and riverine forest; also occurs in the larger gardens, particularly at Fajara where it is a familiar garden bird. Breeding recorded Jan–Sep, but mostly after the start of the rains, Jun–Aug, C/2-3.

[LANIARIUS FERRUGINEUS

Bell Shrike (Tropical Bou-bou)

There are two possible sightings at Abuko: a single bird seen by several observers, Jan 1974 (Jensen & Kirkeby 1980) and one, 6 Feb 1984 (GOS RR) but neither record is considered conclusive.]

349. MALACONOTUS BLANCHOTI (=POLIOCEPHALUS) RB

Grey-headed (or Gladiator) Bush-Shrike

Resident and widespread in open woodland and riverine forest in Lower River but nowhere common; more often heard than seen. Known to have bred annually in Fajara since 1986, Jun–Jul.

350. MALACONOTUS (=CHLOROPHONEUS) SULFUREOPECTUS RB*

Orange- (or Sulphur-) breasted Bush Shrike

Rare resident (*M.s. sulfureopectus*) in woodland and dense thickets; appears to be decreasing with loss of habitat. Recorded in every month from Fajara, Brufut, Abuko, Yundum and Jappeni. Breeding has never been proved, but juvenile seen in Jan.

351. NILAUS AFER ?RB, ?MB

Brubru Shrike (or Northern Brubru)

Probably a scarce resident (*N.a. after*) in woodland but status uncertain. More frequently seen during the rains, Jul–Nov and there are no records Mar–May, which indicates that it may be an intra-African migrant visitor. Recent records from Abuko, Yundum, Keneba, Tendaba, Mansakonko, Sapu and Bansang (Bray *et al*, GOS Rev, GOS ABR 1975–76–77). Adult feeding a fledgling at Abuko, 21 Nov 1987 (J. N. Dymond) is the first evidence of breeding.

352. TCHAGRA SENEGALA RB

Black-crowned Tchagra (or Black-headed Bush-Shrike)

Common resident (*T.s. senegala*) widespread in Lower River, where its melodius song is one of the characteristic sounds in open bush country; less common inland. Breeds Oct–Dec, C/2 usual.

Laniinae

353. CORVINELLA CORVINA RB

Long-tailed (or Yellow-billed) Shrike

Common resident (*C.c. corvina*), in open bush, gardens and along the roadside on the coast and in Lower River; scarce further inland. Breeding season is extended, Mar–Oct, but most nest during the rains, Jul–Oct, C/2-3. Parties of up to 10 occur in the off-season. [In Ghana they are co-operative breeders (Grimes 1987) and there is recent evidence to show that this is the case in The Gambia, notably in the immediate post-fledging period (C. R. Barlow, P. Byass, C. White).]

354. LANIUS COLLURIO AV

Red-backed Shrike

Vagrant from the Palaearctic, only 4 records (*L.c. isabellinus*): one at Banjul Bund, 12 Feb–14 Mar 1965 (Bray *et al.*); a female at Kotu Beach, 29 Nov 1977 (Jensen & Kirkeby 1980); one at Tendaba, 19 Nov 1984 (Ericsson 1989); one (photographed) at Camaloo, 12 Mar 1987 (GOS ABR 1986–87).

355. LANIUS EXCUBITOR AV

Great Grey Shrike

African vagrant (*L.e. leucopygos*); the northwestern Sahara race (*L.e. elegans*) may also occur. There are 5 confirmed records, all singles, three of which were photographed: Soma, 18 Dec 1973 (M. Wallin); Pakali Ba, 22 Dec 1975 (GOS ABR 1975); Cape Road, 5 Jan and 4 Mar 1980 (GOS ABR 1980); Cape St Mary, 12 Apr 1983; Barra, 16 Dec 1983; Banjul, 23 Dec 1983 (GOS RR). There have been several other recent unconfirmed sightings.

356. LANIUS SENATOR PV, WV

Woodchat Shrike

Common Palaearctic passage visitor (*L.s. senator*), Nov and Feb–Mar, in open country in Lower and Middle River; most numerous on northward migration in Mar. A few over-winter.

MUSCICAPIDAE
Turdinae

357. CERCOMELA MELANURA AV

Black-tailed Rock-Chat

African vagrant; the only record is a party of 3–4 seen (and photographed) on an area of hard alluvial ground devoid of any grass but with scattered small trees and bushes, near Fatoto, early Feb 1974 (GOS REV).

358. CERCOTRICHAS (=AGROBATES) GALACTOTES AV

Rufous Scrub-Robin (or Warbler)

Rare African (possibly also Palaearctic *C.g. galactotes*) vagrant (*C.g. minor*); only 5 confirmed records, all singles: near Banjul, 15 Feb 1969, (Morel 1972); Fajara, 1 Jan 1974 (GOS Rev); Camaloo, 24 Mar 1979 (GOS ABR 1979); Cape Road, 1 and 4 Feb 1981 (GOS ABR 1981); Kiang West (photographed), 10 Jan 1986 (GOS RR). There have been several unconfirmed sightings since 1982.

359. COSSYPHA ALBICAPILLA RB

White-crowned Robin-Chat

Not uncommon and widespread resident (*C.a. albicapilla*) in dense cover particularly riverine forest, throughout the country. Most numerous along the river banks in Middle and Upper River; locally common in Lower River; occurs in gardens in Fajara. Breeds Jun–Oct. Nests, all C/2, found in hanging flower pot, fallen palm frond hanging on branch of tree, and at base of pruned frond on palm tree.

360. COSSYPHA NIVEICAPILLA RB

Snowy-crowned (or -headed) Robin-Chat

Uncommon, local resident (*C.n. niveicapilla*) in thick woodland and gallery forest; occasionally in gardens. Most records are from Lower River — Fajara, Abuko, Yundum, Selety — but has been recorded inland to Georgetown. Breeds Jun–Sep, C/3.

361. LUSCINIA MEGARHYNCHOS PV, WV

Nightingale

Not uncommon Palaearctic passage and winter visitor (*L.m. megarhychos*), 15 Nov–27 Mar, most numerous on passage in late Nov; fewer seen on northward passage in spring. Easily overlooked except for the song; regularly heard all winter on the coast, where territories are taken up in the dense cover of low bushes behind the sand-dunes south of Fajara and in gullies along the cliff at Fajara and Brufut. Recorded inland as far as Wallikunda.

362. LUSCINIA SVECICA AV

Bluethroat

Vagrant from the Palaearctic, only 2 records: one at Cape St Mary, 18 Feb 1974 and 3 near Basse, 21 Feb 1974 (Jensen & Kirkeby 1980). A migrant to Senegal and the inundation zone of the Niger.

363. MONTICOLA SAXATILIS (WV)

Rock-Thrush

Previously considered to be a vagrant from the Palaearctic; today it is a rare and irregular winter visitor. Until the 1970s the only record was a specimen from Bathurst (now Banjul) reported by Reichenow (1904) on the authority of Marche & Campiegne. Jensen & Kirkeby (1980) reported several sightings in the mid-1970s which were not included in the first edition as no details had been made available to the GOS. These records, 2 on 31 Dec 1972 and 6 singles, Dec–Mar, have now been seen (*Malimbus* 9: 123–124) and are accepted. There has been one further record — a single near Banjul, 10 Feb 1981 (GOS ABR 1981). Bannerman (1930–51) has records from Casamance and Guinea-Bissau and Morel, Monnet & Rouchhouse have several recent wintering records near Dakar (*Malimbus* 5: 1–4, 1983).

364. MONTICOLA SOLITARIA (WV)

Blue Rock-Thrush

Previously considered a Palaearctic vagrant (*M.s. solitaria*); today it is a rare and irregular winter visitor. Until 1980, there were only 4 records, 3 of which may refer to the same bird: a male on the rocks beneath the cliff at Fajara, 28 Jan–1 Mar 1965 (McGregor & Landsborough Thomson, *Ibis* 107: 401) was the first record for The Gambia. A male, likely to be the same bird, was present in exactly the same area in early 1966 and 1967 (I. A. McGregor). The other record is one at Barra, Jan 1974 (GOS Rev). There were 4 records at Barra and Fajara, Nov–Dec 1980 (GOS ABR 1980). Since 1980 Morel, Monnet & Rouchouse (*Malimbus* 5: 1–4, 1983) have records from Casamance and several annually near Dakar, Senegal indicating that it is a regular winter visitor to this part of the West African coast.

365. MYRMECOCICHLA AETHIOPS DSV, ?RB

Ant-Chat (or Ant-eater Chat)

A regular visitor immediately after the rains; it appears to be spreading southwards and is now possibly a local resident (*M.a. aethiops*) on the North Bank where it has been recorded regularly at Barra and Essau in recent years and from where Lowe collected an unspecified number in 1929 (Bannerman 1930–51). Recently reported inland to Farafenni. There is an undated note by Stevens in the Government Agricultural Department's copy of Bannerman that he had seen it at Sankulakunda on the South Bank. There are two recent records from the South Bank: a party of 6, almost certainly this species, at Soma, Jan 1974 (GOS Rev) and a single at Brumen Bridge, 28 Jan 1984 (GOS RR).

366. MYRMECOCICHLA (=PENTHOLAEA) ALBIFRONS RB*

White-fronted Black Chat

Scarce resident (*M.a. frontalis*), widely but locally distributed in open woodland and clearings throughout the country. Recorded from Yundum, Keneba, and Mansakonko (GOS Rev) and on the roadside between Georgetown and Basse (K. M. Stevens). Display observed at Yundum in Jun and undoubtedly breeds during the rains, Jul–Oct, but no nest has been found.

[OENANTHE DESERTI Rejected

Desert Wheatear

The sighting of a single bird on Fajara golf course, 24 Dec 1972 (Jensen & Kirkeby 1980) is not accepted for this Check-list and needs confirmation.]

367. OENANTHE HISPANICA AV

Spanish (or Black-eared) Wheatear

A vagrant (*O.h. hispanica*) from the Palaearctic. The record in Bannerman (1930–51) for The Gambia was based on a skin in the British Museum merely labelled 'Gambia' which was obtained from a dealer; this is accepted as records from

Senegal were usually marked Senegambia. There are 3 other records all singles, one of which was not accepted in the first edition due to lack of information available at the time: Barra, 10 Feb 1976 (Jensen & Kirkeby 1980); Fajara, a male on 26 Mar 1983 (GOS RR) and Kuntaur, 17 Jan 1989 (P. Donnelly & B. Macdonald).

368. OENANTHE ISABELLINA AV

Isabelline Wheatear

Vagrant from the Palaearctic, one record only: a single bird at Yundum, 23 Feb 1984 for which a rare bird form was completed with full description (GOS RR).

369. OENANTHE OENANTHE PV, WV

Wheatear

Mainly a not uncommon passage visitor (probably *O.o. oenanthe*) from the Palaearctic on open ground; a few over-winter. Most numerous in Lower River, often near the coast, Feb–Mar, but has been recorded throughout the country, Sep–Mar.

370. PHOENICURUS PHOENICURUS PV, WV

Redstart

Not uncommon Palaearctic passage visitor (*P.p. phoenicurus*), usually found in dense cover, sometimes in gardens, Oct–Nov and Feb–Mar. A few over-winter, more often inland than on the coast, occurring in riverine forest, particularly in Middle River; recorded in winter from Mansakonko, Baboon I. and Sapu but there are also recent wintering records from the coast.

371. SAXICOLA RUBETRA PV, WV

Whinchat

Common Palaearctic, mainly passage visitor Oct–Nov and Feb–Mar, on open ground throughout the country but recorded 13 Sep–9 May and the occasional bird overwinters.

372. TURDUS PELIOS (= LIBONYANUS) RB

West African (Olive or Kurrichane) Thrush

Resident (*T.p. chiguancoides*) and common on the edge of forest, and in gardens in Lower River; particularly numerous before and during the rains. Less common inland, though recorded from all areas. Some dispersal takes place during the dry season. Breeds Jun–Oct. C/3 usual.

Timaliinae

373. PHYLLANTHUS ATRIPENNIS ?

Capuchin Babbler

Status unknown. Bannerman (1930–51) refers to one skin from The Gambia in the British Museum without data. A bird of dense cover, Cawkell & Moreau state that it was 'recorded once by Cawkell (no date given). Suitable habitat is now rare.' Only recent record is *c.* 4 in thick secondary growth in Sukuta woods, 26 May and 2 June 1979 (GOS ABR 1979).

374. TURDOIDES PLEBEJUS RB

Brown Babbler

Abundant resident (*T.p. platycircus*) in open bush and in woodland bordering cleared agricultural land; a familiar garden bird. Breeds during the rains, Jun–Oct or longer; a party with a young *Clamator levaillantii* seen 9 Jan (Bray *et al.*).

375. TURDOIDES REINWARDII RB

Blackcap Babbler

Resident (*T.r. reinwardii*) and common in open bush, gardens, etc, but not as numerous as *T.plebejus*. Breeds Jun–Oct.

Sylviinae

376. ACROCEPHALUS ARUNDINACEUS AV

Great Reed Warbler

Vagrant from the Palaearctic, only 4 records: near Banjul, one trapped and ringed, Nov 1971 (G. Johansen); Basse, one on 21 Feb 1974 (Jensen & Kirkeby 1980); Sapu, one in Nov 1975 (K. & C. Carlson); Camaloo, one on 4 Sep 1980 (GOS ABR 1980). The record of one at Banjul, 22 Feb 1984, was not accepted (GOS RR).

377. ACROCEPHALUS BOETICATUS ?RB

African Reed Warbler

Status uncertain, possibly resident. The only records are of 5 nests, two C/3 and three C/2 in reedbeds at Kotu, Bakau and Camaloo, collected by Walton, Jul 1945 (Cawkell & Moreau). Probably still occurs but overlooked.

[ACROCEPHALUS PALUSTRIS

Marsh Warbler

The only probable records are of one seen and heard singing Kotu Stream, 24 Feb 1974 (Jensen & Kirkeby 1980) and one heard on Banjul Bund, early Nov 1977 (GOS ABR 1977), but no details are available, merely that the observers were familiar with the song in Europe.]

378. ACROCEPHALUS SCHOENOBAENUS PV, WV

Sedge Warbler

Uncommon Palaearctic passage and winter visitor, occurring in tangled undergrowth, usually adjacent to water or reed-beds, and probably largely overlooked. First recorded along Banjul Bund, Jan 1969, and 4 at Pakalinding the same month (GOS Rev). The only records since are: Banjul, one trapped and ringed, Mar 1971 (G. Johansen), total of 6 singing late Feb 1975, 3 on 20 Dec 1975 (GOS ABR 1975); Camaloo, 2–3 on 28 Jan 1978, Feb and Nov 1979 (GOS ABR 1978–79); one near Cape St Mary, 14 Nov 1984 (Ericsson 1989); Georgetown, one on 26 Nov 1987; total of 6 singles recorded on tour of country, Nov 1988 (J. N. Dymond). Serle *et al.* describes it as 'very common on passage on the lower Senegal River.'

379. ACROCEPHALUS SCIRPACEUS PV, WV

Reed Warbler

Uncommon Palaearctic passage and winter visitor (*A.s. scirpaceus*), probably largely overlooked. Cawkell & Moreau state that it has twice been collected in winter (no details given) and Cawkell heard it singing on 27 Dec 1960, 22 Jan (4), 12 Mar and 2 Apr 1961. Heard singing Banjul Bund, Nov–Dec 1965; a total of 14 trapped and ringed near Banjul, Nov–Mar between 1969 and 1974 (G. Johansen); reported in mangrove Jan 1972 and Jan 1975 (GOS Rev), up to 4 Jan–Feb 1975 (GOS ABR 1975) and Jan 1976 (GOS ABR 1976); a few annually since.

380. APALIS FLAVIDA (=CANICEPS) RB*

Yellow-chested Apalis

Rare and local resident (*A.f. caniceps?*) in remnant forest in Lower River but breeding has never been proved. Regularly recorded in and around Abuko Nature Reserve where it was first seen on 27 Feb 1969 (Morel 1972), the records are: up to 4 seen and heard on several occasions between 12 and 23 Dec 1975 (GOS ABR 1975), 2 on 13 Mar 1977 (GOS ABR 1977), 4–5, Dec 1979 (GOS ABR 1979), up to 6 on several occasions, Jan 1983, 4 on 26 Feb 1984 (GOS RR); 2 on 16 Nov 1984 (Ericsson 1989). 2–3 near Sibanor, 29 Mar 1979 (GOS ABR 1979) is the only record from elsewhere. Its presence in The Gambia is a considerable extension of its range; previously not known to occur west of Ghana.

381. CAMAROPTERA BRACHYURA (=BREVICAUDATA) RB

Grey-backed Camaroptera

Common resident (*C.b. brevicaudata*) in open woodland and bush, also in gardens. Breeds Jun–Oct, C/2 usual.

382. CAMAROPTERA CHLORONATA AV

Green-backed Camaroptera

African vagrant, 2 records only: one at Abuko, 24 Jan 1984 (Morel & Morel in prep.) and one observed in the canopy at close range for several minutes from a high observation platform in Pirang forest, Oct 1986 (G.G.F.P.).

383. CISTICOLA BRACHYPTERA ?RB ?MB

Shortwing (or Siffling) Cisticola

Not uncommon and widespread (*C.b. brachyptera*) in open grassland with scattered thickets and trees, most numerous in Lower River. Dispersal probably occurs during the dry season as all recent records are during the rains, Jul–Sep, when it breeds, C/3.

384. CISTICOLA CANTANS RB

Singing Cisticola

Resident (*C.c. swanzii*) and not uncommon in the immediate coastal hinterland, but has been recorded 100 km inland; particularly common on the fringes of woodland near Brufut. Breeding, recorded Apr–May, C/3, probably continues into the rains until Aug. Dispersal occurs after breeding.

385. CISTICOLA ERYTHROPS RB

Red-faced Cisticola

Locally common resident (*C.e. erythrops*) in areas of tall grass and scattered bushes in Lower River. Breeding recorded May–Jun, C/3, but probably throughout the rains until Nov, since singing is heard until then. Dispersal occurs after breeding.

386. CISTICOLA GALACTOTES RB

Rufous Grass-Warbler (or Winding Cisticola)

Confined to swampy areas, where it is a locally common resident (*C.g. amphilecta*), throughout the country. Considered to be the common cisticola in grass and reeds at Sapu and Jakhaly (GOS ABR 1975). Breeding recorded Sep, C/3-4, but probably throughout the rains, Jul–Oct.

387. CISTICOLA JUNCIDIS RB

Common Fantail Warbler (or Zitting Cisticola)

Common resident (*C.j. uropygialis*) in grassland adjoining swamps throughout the country. Breeds Jul–Oct, C/4-5. The only cisticola which is to be seen commonly throughout the year.

388. CISTICOLA LATERALIS RB

Whistling Cisticola

Scarce resident widely distributed in open scrubland. Walton collected C/2, 2 Jul (Cawkell & Moreau). Jensen & Kirkeby (1980) have several records from Lower River and one from Middle River. Dispersal occurs after breeding.

389. CISTICOLA NATALENSIS RB

Striped (or Croaking) Cisticola

Scarce resident (*C.n. strangei*). Recent records from open scrub at Cape St Mary, Kiang West, Tendaba and Sapu. Breeding recorded Aug–Sep, C/2; family party of 5 at Sapu, 24 Oct 1974 (GOS Rev).

390. CISTICOLA RUFA ?

Rufous Cisticola

Status uncertain. Morel (1972) refers to 1–2 at Fajara on 16 Jan (no year given) and 'one other observation' (undated) in Lower River from his own unedited notes. The only other records are 3–4 at Abuko before 1969 (GOS Rev — source not traced) and a single at Kiang West, 7 Jan 1986 (GOS RR).

391. CISTICOLA RUFICEPS ?

Redpate Cisticola

Status unknown. Bannerman (1930–51) refers to specimens (*C.r. guinea*) collected at Kuntaur, India (location not traced, possibly Medina) and Farafenni, and K. M. Stevens, in a manuscript note in the Government Agricultural Department's copy of Bannerman, records having seen it on the north bank in Dec 1947. Only accepted record since is one at Kiang West, 7 Jan 1986 (GOS RR).

392. EREMOMELA PUSILLA RB

(Smaller) Green-backed Eremomela

Resident (*E.p. pusilla)*) and common in woodland throughout the country. Breeding recorded, Apr, C/2, but probably continues into the rains Jul–Oct.

393. HIPPOLAIS PALLIDA PV, WV

Olivaceous Warbler

Not uncommon Palaearctic passage and winter visitor (*H.p. opaca*), 25 Jul–5 May, in dense scrub, sometimes in overgrown gardens, particularly at Fajara where they are present throughout the winter. Most recorded on migration, Oct–Nov and Mar, when parties of 5–10 occur.

394. HIPPOLAIS POLYGLOTTA PV, WV

Melodious Warbler

Common Palaearctic passage visitor (some over-winter) in open bush, thickets, gardens, etc, recorded Sep to May, most frequently Oct and Feb–Mar, when it is a familiar garden bird at Fajara.

395. HYLIA PRASINA RB

Green Hylia

Scarce and local resident confined to remnant forest in Lower River. First recorded in Abuko Nature Reserve where it is resident, 15 May 1969 (Morel 1972), regularly since 1974 and many recent records 1981–89; a pair feeding well developed young, 15 Jan 1981 (GOS ABR 1981) was the first evidence of breeding. Only record from elsewhere is Sukuta woods (now felled), near Abuko, on 12 Aug 1979 (GOS ABR 1979) though birds believed to be this species seen on several occasions at Pirang, Mar 1985 and Oct 1986 (G.G.F.P.). (The birds in Abuko were originally identified as Black-capped Woodland Warblers *Siecercus herberti* (GOS Rev, GOS ABR 1975) but from a detailed description, including the call, of several observed at close range on 20 Apr 1977 this was corrected (GOS ABR 1977) and *S. herberti* was deleted from The Gambia list.)

396. HYPERGERUS ATRICEPS RB

Moho (or Oriole Warbler)

Local but not uncommon resident, usually in the vicinity of water, in the thick scrub immediately behind the sand-dunes on the coast, at Kotu and Tanji, at Abuko Nature Reserve and in the tall *Rhizophora* mangrove and riverine forest along Middle and Upper River to Bansang; not recorded further inland. Breeds Jun–Nov, C/3 usual.

397. LOCUSTELLA NAEVIA AV

Grasshopper Warbler

Vagrant from the Palaearctic, one confirmed record only: a single bird in coastal scrub near Kotu Stream, 27 Dec 1980 (GOS ABR 1980). An earlier record of a single bird at Camaloo, 26 Feb 1976 (Jensen & Kirkeby 1980) was not accepted.

398. PHYLLOSCOPUS BONELLI PV, WV

Bonelli's Warbler

Scarce Palaearctic migrant (*P.b. bonelli*). Until 1978 there were only 5 records: Banjul, one on 30 Dec 1960 and 11 Jan 1961 (Cawkell & Moreau), and 30 Nov 1968; Fajara, 2 in Dec 1973; Abuko Nature Reserve, one in Jan 1974 (GOS Rev). There were several records in 1978, all at Fajara: 11 Jan and 9 Feb and again between 8 and 23 Dec, 3 on 19 Dec and regular Jan–Mar, 28 Apr, 21 May, Sep and Nov 1979 (GOS ABR 1978–79). Reported regularly since 1980.

399. PHYLLOSCOPUS COLLYBITA PV, WV

Chiffchaff

Common Palaearctic passage and winter visitor (*P.c. collybita*), 25 Oct–3 May. Most numerous Dec–Feb, indicating that the majority are winter visitors. Particularly associated with the small mangrove *Avicennia*, but also occurs in gardens and open woodland and scrub with scattered trees. One ringed in UK, Sep 1970, was recovered in The Gambia, Jan 1971.

400. PHYLLOSCOPUS SIBILATRIX AV

Wood Warbler

Vagrant from the Palaearctic; only record is one clearly identified at a bird bath at Fajara, 4 May 1979 (GOS ABR 1979). There was a possible sighting near Cape St Mary, 24 Mar 1975 (GOS Rev). Very occasionally occurs as far west as Senegal (Serle *et al.* 1977).

401. PHYLLOSCOPUS TROCHILUS PV, WV

Willow Warbler

Common Palaearctic passage visitor (*P.t. trochilus*) in open woodland, forest edge and gardens; mainly Oct–Nov and Mar, but some over-winter and has been recorded between 16 Aug and 5 May.

402. PRINIA (=HELIOLAIS) ERYTHROPTERA RB

Red-winged Warbler

Scarce and local resident (*P.e. erythroptera*) in dense bush in Lower and Middle River; recorded Banjul, Cape St Mary, Yundum, Brufut, Keneba and Sapu. Recorded from Upper River only at Bansang. Breeds Jun–Sep, C/3.

403. PRINIA SUBFLAVA RB

West African (or Tawny-flanked) Prinia

Common resident (*P.s. subflava*), widely distributed in open bush throughout the country. Breeds Aug–Dec, C/3 usual. (A new species *Prinia fluviatilis*, The River Prinia, has recently been described which occurs in Senegal (Chappuis 1974, Chappuis *et al.* 1988). It is found in the vicinity of water and is separated from *P. subflava* principally by its song. It is possible that this species also occurs in The Gambia.)

[SPHENOEACUS (=MELOCICHLA) MENTALIS

Moustached Warbler

Jensen & Kirkeby (1980) have one record from Banjul Bund, 18 Dec 1973, but confirmation is needed.]

404. SYLVIA ATRICAPILLA PV, WV

Blackcap

Palaearctic passage and winter visitor (*S.a. atricapilla*). Status varies depending upon the harshness of the winter in the Mediterranean basin; in Lower River quite common when it is cold in the north, less so if it is milder. Occurs in open scrubland with scattered trees, mangrove and gardens. Recorded 16 Nov–11 May.

405. SYLVIA BORIN PV, WV

Garden Warbler

Not uncommon Palaearctic passage visitor; a few over-winter. Occurs in open woodland, gardens and scrubland bordering mangrove. Most recorded on southward passage, Oct–Nov, but an individual remained in a garden at Cape St Mary, 1 Dec–15 Feb and another at Yundum throughout Jan and Feb.

406. SYLVIA CANTILLANS WV

Subalpine Warbler

Scarce but regular Palaearctic winter visitor. No evidence of any increase during normal months of passage. Particularly associated with Acacia bushes and mangrove in Lower River from the coast to Tendaba, but has been recorded inland in thick scrub at Jakhaly.

407. SYLVIA COMMUNIS PV, WV

European Whitethroat

Scarce Palaearctic passage and winter visitor (*S.c. communis*) in dense scrub, Oct–Mar. Most records are from the belt of scrub behind the sand-dunes on the coast, Nov–Jan; once seen inland at Kaiaff in Jan.

[SYLVIA CONSPICILLATA

Spectacled Warbler

Two possible records: a bird reported as being this species in coastal scrub, 21 Mar 1981, and one near the Senegambia Hotel, Fajara, 27 Mar 1983. These were not accepted as insufficient details were supplied, though the observer of the 1983 bird was familiar with this species from elsewhere (GOS ABR 1981, GOS RR). Browne (*Malimbus* 4. 1982) identifies south-west Mauritania as being its principal southern wintering ground and it is possible that occasionally an individual might stray further south into The Gambia. There is one record from Senegal (Morel & Morel in prep.).

408. SYLVIA HORTENSIS AV

Orphean Warbler

Vagrant from the Palaearctic (*S.h. hortensis*). Only 4 accepted records but several other probables: Banjul, one on 5 Jan 1969 (GOS Rev); Barra, one seen 15

Dec and the same or another bird trapped and photographed, 23 Dec 1983 (M. Wallin); Brufut, one on 16 Dec 1975 (GOS ABR 1975); Yundum, one on 23 Nov 1987 (J. N. Dymond). There have been 4 other recent records, all in Lower River: Dec 1983, Jan and Feb 1984 and Feb 1987; these have not been accepted because insufficient details were supplied by the observers (GOS RR).

409. SYLVIETTA BRACHYURA — RB

Nuthatch Warbler (or Crombec)

Resident and widely distributed (*S.b. brachyura*) in open bush and woodland in Lower and Middle River, but nowhere common; not recorded from Upper River. Breeding recorded May–Jun, C/2.

410. SYLVIETTA DENTI — AV

Lemon- (or White-) bellied Crombec

African vagrant, only 3 records: one in thick forest near Tanji, 16 Apr 1964; one near Brufut, 22 Apr 1964 (G. & P. Gore per E. M. Cawkell); a pair near Jakhaly, 5 Nov 1975 (not 1976 as in 1st Edition) (full description received from K. & C. Carlson).

Muscicapinae

411. BRADORNIS PALLIDUS — RB

Pale Flycatcher

A rare resident (*B.p. modestus*) in open woodland, mainly confined to Lower River but it is easily overlooked and may be more widely distributed. Regularly reported in recent years at Yundum, where fledged young were being fed in Jun. The only other recent records are from Abuko, Pirang, Batabut and once in Upper River near Basse.

412. FICEDULA HYPOLEUCA — PV, WV

Pied Flycatcher

Mainly a not uncommon Palaearctic passage visitor (*F.h. hypoleuca*) in autumn, occurring in open bush, gardens. Earliest record 24 Aug; most occur Sep–Nov. A few Dec–Jan records. Rare on northwards passage, Feb–May.

[FRASERIA CINERASCENS — Rejected

White-browed Forest Flycatcher

The record of one at Abuko, 29 Jan 1974 (Jensen & Kirkeby 1980) seen by one observer is not acceptable.]

413. MELAENORNIS EDOLIOIDES — RB

Black Flycatcher

Not uncommon resident widely distributed in open woodland throughout the country; occasionally in gardens. Breeds Jun–Oct. Nest building at Yundum in Jun and Brufut in Jul; young seen Jul–Oct.

414. MUSCICAPA (=ALSEONAX) AQUATICA RB

Swamp Flycatcher

There was for some years doubt as to whether the small brown flycatcher which is resident and common along the riverbank from Baboon I. to the east of the country was *M. aquatica* or *M. cassini*. A specimen collected in Feb 1978 (M. E. J. Gore) was subsequently identified at the British Museum (P. R. Colston) as *M.a. aquatica*. Breeds during the rains, Jul–Oct, feeding young in Nov.

415. MUSCICAPA STRIATA PV, WV

Spotted Flycatcher

Not uncommon Palaearctic passage and winter visitor (*M.s. striata*), 10 Sep–24 Mar in open bush, gardens, etc. Most recorded on passage Sep–Oct, smaller numbers Feb–Mar; a few over-winter. Recorded from the coast inland to Bansang.

416. MYIOPARUS (=PARISOMA) PLUMBEUS RB*

Grey Tit-Babbler (or Flycatcher)

Rare and local (*M.p. plumbeus*), but widely distributed, resident in remnant high open forest. Recorded recently from Tanji, Pirang, Kabafitta, Jambur, Tendaba, Jakhaly and Basse. Probably breeds, but there is no evidence.

Platysteirinae

417. BATIS SENEGALENSIS RB

Senegal Puff-back Flycatcher

Uncommon local resident in woodland in Lower River. Numbers appear to be decreasing almost certainly as a result of loss of habitat. Breeding season is mainly May–Jul, but nesting has been reported as early as Mar.

418. BIAS MUSICUS AV

Black-and-White Flycatcher

Rare African vagrant, one record only: a male singing from an exposed branch in a tall tree in cleared agricultural land near the forest edge at Selety, 12 May 1976 (GOS ABR 1976). Not previously recorded north of Guinea Bissau.

419. MEGABYAS FLAMMULATA AV

Shrike-Flycatcher

Rare African vagrant, one record only: a single bird seen by a group of observers in Abuko Nature Reserve, 1 Dec 1988 (C. R. Barlow, J. Gooders *et al.*). Not previously recorded north of Sierra Leone.

420. PLATYSTEIRA CYANEA RB

Scarlet-spectacled Wattle-eye

Resident (*P.c. cyanea*), widely distributed and not uncommon in Lower and Middle River, often in *Avicennia* mangrove; also occurs in riverine forest and open woodland, occasionally in gardens. Breeding season is probably mainly during the rains, Jul–Oct, but extends from 16 May (displaying) to Dec (pair with 2 young).

Monarchinae

421. HYLIOTA FLAVIGASTER — RB*

Yellow-bellied Flycatcher

Scarce resident (*H.f. flavigaster*) in high open forest and woodland; all records are from Lower and Middle River. Breeding never proved.

422. TERPSIPHONE (= TCHITREA) RUFIVENTER — RB

Red-bellied Paradise Flycatcher

See *T. viridis*.

423. TERPSIPHONE (= TCHITREA) VIRIDIS — RB

Paradise Flycatcher

Since *T. rufiventer* and *T. viridis*, both of which are not uncommon residents, have frequently been seen together and courting indiscriminately, it seems probable that they are, in fact, conspecific. *T. rufiventer*, all-rufous below or with varying amounts of blue-grey on the rufous underparts, is commonest in Lower River but also occurs in Middle and Upper River; *T. viridis* occurs mainly in Middle and Upper River. Both are found in open woodland, gardens. Breeding recorded May–Jul, C/2 usual.

424. TROCHOCERCUS (= ERANNORNIS) LONGICAUDA — ?RB

Blue Fairy Flycatcher

Rare, probably resident (*T.l. longicauda*), sparsely distributed on the forest edge along Middle and Upper River from Tendaba eastwards. Recently regularly reported from the north bank opposite Tendaba; also from Baboon I., Wallikunda, Bansang and Fatoto. Breeding never proved and may be only a non-breeding visitor from the upper reaches of the Gambia River in Senegal where it is not uncommon, but there are recent records for most months and it seems likely that it is in fact resident.

REMIZIDAE

425. REMIZ (= ANTHOSCOPUS) PARVULUS — RB

West African (or Yellow) Penduline Tit

Scarce resident in open forest; recorded from Brufut, Yundum, Keneba, Mansakonko and Bansang. Only breeding record is Mar.

[REMIZ (= ANTHOSCOPUS) PUNCTIFRONS — Rejected

Sudan (Sennar) Penduline Tit

The 1975 record in GOS Rev and GOS ABR 1975 was an error and was deleted from the The Gambia list in GOS ABR 1976.]

PARIDAE

426. PARUS LEUCOMELAS (=MELANIPARUS NIGER) RB

White-shouldered Black Tit

Scarce resident (*P.l. guineensis*), widely but locally distributed in open woodland in Lower River; rare in Middle River and not recorded from Upper River. Breeds Jan–May.

CERTHIIDAE

427. SALPORNIS SPILONOTA AV

Spotted Creeper

African vagrant, 3 records only: one in a newly burnt area of scrubland near Bondali, 17 Mar 1963 (Cawkell 1965); 2 on the edge of dense forest near Keneba, 15 May 1976 (GOS ABR 1976); and one in Abuko Nature Reserve early Dec 1977 (GOS ABR 1977).

NECTARINIIDAE

428. ANTHREPTES COLLARIS RB

Collared Sunbird

Scarce resident (*A.c. subcollaris*) in forest; all records from Lower River. Appears to have become more common over the past 10–15 years. Bannerman (1930–51) refers to specimens in the Bremen Museum labelled 'from Gambia', but neither Hopkinson nor Cawkell encountered it. Since 1973 there have been regular sightings in Abuko Nature Reserve, Fajara, Howbah, Kabafitta and Sukuta woods. Breeds during the rains; pair feeding 2 fledged young at Pirang, Oct 1986 (G.G.F.P.) and at Abuko Nature Reserve, Oct 1988 (C. R. Barlow).

429. ANTHREPTES GABONICUS RB

Mouse-brown Sunbird

Scarce resident on the coast and along Lower River inland to Tendaba, confined to mangrove and the belt of trees immediately behind. Breeding first proved 2 Dec 1986, when adult seen at nest on tip of mangrove branch; another at nest, 1 Dec 1987 (J. N. Dymond).

430. ANTHREPTES LONGUEMAREI RB

Violet-backed Sunbird

Scarce resident (*A.l. longuemarei*) widely distributed in Lower and Middle River, often associated with the small mangrove *Avicennia*, but also occurs in open woodland. Reported from Brufut, Yundum, Pirang, Keneba, Tendaba, Kaiaff, Mansakonko and Sapu. Breeding first confirmed at Yundum, May 1980 (GOS ABR 1980).

431. ANTHREPTES (=HEDYDIPNA) PLATURA RB

Pigmy Long-tailed Sunbird

Scarce resident (*A.p. platura*) in dry bush and woodland. Appears to be more numerous inland than near the coast, though regularly reported from Fajara.

Breeds Jan–Mar, one record Sep, C/2; often nests in association with wasp (Cawkell & Moreau).

432. NECTARINIA (=CINNYRIS) COCCINIGASTER R

Splendid Sunbird

Resident and locally common in open woodland and gardens in Lower Rive scarce further inland as far as Sapu. Breeds during the rains, Jul–Sep.

433. NECTARINIA (=CINNYRIS) CUPREA R

Copper Sunbird

Not uncommon resident (*N.c. cuprea*) in secondary and open woodland. Mo probably a local migrant, moving south during the dry season. Breeds before an during the rains, May–Oct, usually C/3.

434. NECTARINIA PULCHELLA R

Beautiful Long-tailed Sunbird

Common resident (*N.p. pulchella*), a familiar garden bird. Most numerou in Lower River but occurs throughout the country. Breeding season extende Cawkell & Moreau state that nesting usually coincides with the rains, Jul–Oct an Hopkinson (Bannerman 1930–51) reported breeding in Banjul in Jun, but all recen breeding records are after the rains, Nov–Mar.

435. NECTARINIA (=CHALCOMITRA) SENEGALENSIS R

Scarlet-breasted (or -chested) Sunbird

Widely distributed and not uncommon resident (*N.s. senegalensis*) in ope bush across the whole country. More common up-river, where it is usually the onl sunbird encountered. Breeds Apr–Jul.

436. NECTARINIA (=CINNYRIS) VENUSTA R

Yellow-bellied (or Variable) Sunbird

Locally common and resident (*N.v. venusta*) in Lower River, particular numerous in the belt of dense scrub and scattered trees inland from the sand-dune on the coast; rare in Middle River and not recorded from Upper River. Breed Mar–Apr.

437. NECTARINIA (=CYANOMITRA) VERTICALIS RB

Olive-backed (or Green-headed) Sunbird

Rare resident (*N.v. verticalis*), confined to Lower River woodland, usually i the vicinity of water. No nest has ever been found, but an immature believed to b this species was seen at Kotu Stream, 30 Aug; may therefore breed during the rains

ZOSTEROPIDAE

438. ZOSTEROPS SENEGALENSIS R

Yellow White-eye

Scarce, local resident (*Z.s. senegalensis*) in open woodland, occasionally i gardens. Until recently recorded only from Lower River: at Cape St Mary 'undum, Keneba and Tendaba. There are now records from Mansakonko and akhaly in Middle River and Darsilami in Upper River and it is clear the species is istributed throughout the country. Evidence of breeding is an immature seen at 'undum in May.

EMBERIZIDAE

39. EMBERIZA FORBESI MB*

Nigerian Little (or Brown-rumped) Bunting

A scarce and local wet season visitor (*E.f. nigeriae*), remaining until the start of ne dry season; locally common inland from Kiang West, Jun–Oct, where singing nales were present 1974 and 1975; none seen there Mar and May (GOS Rev, GOS BR 1975). Also recorded during the likely breeding season at Mansakonko and apu. Rare on the coast: a small party (number not given) at Kotu, May 1966 and ne at Tanji, 16 Nov 1986 (C. R. Barlow) indicate movement before and after esting. One at Sapu, Mar 1975 (GOS Rev) is an unusual dry season record. Jndoubtedly breeds but no nest has ever been found.

40. EMBERIZA HORTULANA AV

Ortolan Bunting

Rare vagrant from the Palaearctic, 2 records only: a single bird at Banjul und, 11–16 Nov 1955 (Bray *et al.*) and a male at Tendaba, 3 Apr 1981 (GOS ABR 981).

41. EMBERIZA (=FRINGILLARIA) STRIOLATA AV

Saharan House-Bunting

African vagrant, 3 records only: Albreda, a pair, one of which was captured, ec 1926 (Hopkinson in Bannerman 1930–51); Barra, one (photographed) 10 Feb 976 (Jensen & Kirkeby 1980) and a single 18 Nov 1982 (GOS RR).

42. EMBERIZA (=FRINGILLARIA) TAHAPSI MB

(Cinnamon-breasted) Rock-Bunting

Not uncommon but local migrant breeding visitor (*E.t. goslingi*), nesting nmediately after the rains. All records are between Nov and Mar. Nest C/2 near apu, where at least 2 singing males were present in open bush on stony hill, early ov 1975 (GOS ABR 1975). Recorded from similar terrain at Tendaba, Jan 1974 GOS Rev). Only records from the coast are Banjul Bund, 9–15 Nov 1965 and 20 Iar 1967, and Cape St Mary, 5 Nov 1966 (Bray *et al.*).

FRINGILLIDAE

43. SERINUS (=POLIOSPIZA) LEUCOPYGIUS RB*

Grey Canary (or White-rumped Seed-eater)

Hopkinson (Bannerman 1930–51) described it as fairly common (*S.l. genbachi*) 'numbers increasing the further we get from the sea'. In 1979 (from the w records) it was considered scarce and confined to cleared agricultural land and oen bush, often around villages, in Middle and Upper River. Since then it has creased, and today it is frequently reported in Lower River and on the coast.

Breeding has never been proved. Quite common in Senegal in open country north of The Gambia, and around Dakar, 1975–76 (M. E. J. Gore); doubtless a southward extension of its range has occurred since then linked to desertification.

444. SERINUS MOZAMBICUS RB

Yellow-fronted Canary

Common resident (*S.m. caniceps*) in open woodland and agricultural land with scattered trees. In the 1970s mainly confined to Middle and Upper River and considered scarce nearer the coast but it has increased and today is common throughout the country. Breeds Oct–Nov, usually C/3.

ESTRILDIDAE

445. AMADINA FASCIATA DSV

Cut-throat Weaver

Scarce dry season visitor (*A.f. fasciata*) in open country with scattered trees and in open bush, Oct–Jun. Most numerous in Middle River, arriving Sapu late Oct; also recorded in Upper River near Basse, Nov. Rare in Lower River to the coast, mostly Feb–Apr.

446. AMANDAVA (=ESTRILDA) SUBFLAVA (DSV)

Zebra Waxbill

Hopkinson (Bannerman 1930–51) considered it (*A.s. subflava*) common but local, in swamps, with flocks up to 50 in the dry season. Today it is rare. Very few recent records: Banjul Bund, a single, a pair and a party of 5, Dec 1968 and Jan 1969, a single seen twice, Jan 1972; Camaloo, 4 in Jan 1974 (GOS Rev); Cape St Mary, 2 on 13 Dec 1975 (GOS ABR 1975); Wallikunda, a small flock, 19 July 1980 (GOS ABR 1980). A sighting at Tendaba, 23 Dec 1985 was not accepted (GOS RR). No evidence of breeding.

[ESTRILDA ASTRILD Rejected

Waxbill

The statement in Cawkell & Moreau that the waxbill is 'now commoner by far than *Estrilda melpoda*', is the opposite of that of Hopkinson (1919) who reported it as 'distinctly rare'. Cawkell (1965) subsequently corrected his statement and added that he did not, in fact, record it. The GOS have no recent records and Morel considers a record from Casamance, Senegal to be a misidentification. Serle *et al.* give its range as Sierra Leone to Gabon; also Cape Verde, where probably introduced. As it seems likely that there has been confusion with *E. troglodytes* it is removed from the list.]

447. ESTRILDA (=URAEGINTHUS) BENGALA RB

Red-cheeked Cordon-bleu

Common resident (*E.b. bengala*) throughout the country; a familiar garden bird. Breeding season is extended, Apr–Jan, though mostly during the rains, Jul–Oct, C/3 usual.

448. ESTRILDA (=LAGONOSTICTA) CAERULESCENS RB

Lavender Fire-Finch (or Red-tailed Lavender Waxbill)

Not uncommon resident in open bush, on the edge of cultivated fields, gardens, etc., widely distributed throughout the country and appears to be increasing. Breeding recorded Aug–Oct.

449. ESTRILDA LARVATA (=LAGONOSTICTA NIGRICOLLIS) RB*

Black-faced Fire-Finch

Scarce resident (*E.l. vinacea*) widely distributed in woodland in Lower and Middle River. Recorded from Yundum, Brikama, Keneba, Tendaba, Jakhaly and Sapu. There are no breeding records.

450. ESTRILDA MELPODA RB

Orange-cheeked Waxbill

Resident and locally common on Lower and Middle River, usually in the vicinity of water. Breeding recorded Sep–Nov.

451. ESTRILDA TROGLODYTES RB*

Black-rumped Waxbill

Local but not uncommon inland (*E.t. troglodytes*) in open bush, often in the vicinity of water. Flocks reported from Keneba and Sapu; up to 50 observed gathering at laterite pools, Aug–Nov at Bansang. Scarce near the coast where all records are of parties up to 10 in the Banjul area, Aug–Oct, indicating some dispersal in the non-breeding season. Breeding has never been proved but could occur at the start of the rains from Jun to Aug or, possibly, immediately after the rains, Dec–Jan.

452. LAGONSTICTA RUFOPICTA RB

Bar-breasted Fire-Finch

A scarce and very local resident (*L.r. rufopicta*). Hopkinson (Bannerman 1930–51) described it as local but quite common when present, adding that 'its usual haunts are near water, where it frequents the bush near the iron-stone ridges at the bases of which the birds are fond of gathering'. Few recent records — pairs or small parties at Fajara, Kotu, Yundum, Jakhaly, Sapu and Fatoto. Seen carrying nesting material at Marakissa, Aug 1989.

453. LAGONSTICTA SENEGALA RB

Senegal (or Red-billed) Fire-Finch

Abundant resident (*L.s. senegala*) throughout the country in towns and villages; also occurs in open bush. Appears to breed throughout the year.

454. LONCHURA (=SPERMESTES) CUCULLATA RB

Bronze Mannikin

Abundant resident (*L.c. cucullata*) in towns and villages throughout the country. Breeds Sep–Dec.

455. LONCHURA (=AMAURESTHES) FRINGILLOIDES

Magpie Mannikin

Previously common and apparently resident. Hopkinson (Bannerman 1930–51) considered them as very common in the early part of the century, when he ofte saw them in bird-catchers' cages and sometimes encountered thousands in Banjul i Jun. He noticed that numbers declined drastically after about 1918 'since when the have almost disappeared'. Only recent record is of parties of 2–3 birds, usually i company with *L. cucullata*, seen sporadically at Bakau, Nov–Jan 1973–4 (GO Rev). The reason for their decline is not known.

456. LONCHURA MALABARICA (=EUODICE CANTANS) R

Warbling Silver-bill

A scarce resident (*L.m. cantans*) of Lower and Middle River. Most records ar near the coast, but once at Farafenni, Nov 1986 (C. White). Juveniles seen beggin for food in Oct.

457. NESOCHARIS CAPISTRATA A

White-cheeked Olive Weaver (or Grey-headed Olive-back)

African vagrant; there is one old specimen in the BMNH from The Gambi (Bannerman 1930–51). No other records except a possible sighting in Abuko Natur Reserve, 25 May, no year given (GOS Rev).

458. NIGRITA BICOLOR A

Chestnut-breasted Negro-Finch

African vagrant, only 5 records (all singles): Abuko Nature Reserve, 12 Oc 1968, 18 Sep 1974 (GOS Rev), 18 and 21 Dec 1975 (GOS ABR 1975); Jambu woods, 26 Jun 1979 (GOS ABR 1979). A single reported at Abuko Nature Reserv 14 Jan 1984, was not accepted as no details were supplied (GOS RR). There is possible record of 4–5 at Pirang, May 1985 but identification was uncertai (G.G.F.P.).

459. ORTYGOSPIZA ATRICOLLIS R

Quail-Finch

Locally common resident (*O.a. atricollis*) in grassland bordering swamp throughout the country. Flocks up to 30 reported from Camaloo, Kaiaf Mansakonko, Sapu and Fatoto. Breeding recorded Nov 1977 (C/2) and Nov 197 (C/5) at Camaloo (M. E. Smalley).

460. PIRENESTES OSTRINUS

(Black-bellied) Seed-cracker

Status uncertain. Bannerman (1930–51) cites 4 old skins in the BMNH bu adds that there is some doubt as to the locality from which they actually came. Th only other records are 5 in dense thicket bordering swamp at Jabang, 26 Apr and 3 May 1959 (Cawkell 1960) and 2 near Wallikunda/Sapu, Aug 1980 (GOS AB 1980). There is also one doubtful record from Abuko Nature Reserve, 2 Apr 198 (GOS RR).

61. PYTILIA MELBA AV

Melba Finch (or Green-winged Pytilia)

African vagrant; Lowe collected one (*P.m. citerior*) at Nokunda in Jan 1929 nd another was seen in the same area by Hopkinson later in the year (Bannerman 930–51). No records since.

62. PYTILIA PHOENICOPTERA RB

Red-winged Pytilia

Rare resident (*P.p. phoenicoptera*) but widely scattered in woodland from the oast east to Basse. Breeding recorded in Aug.

63. SPERMOPHAGA HAEMATINA RB

Blue-billed Weaver (or Blue-bill)

A scarce and local resident (*S.h. haematina*) confined to the remnant dense uinea savanna on the south bank in Lower River. Resident in Abuko Nature eserve; recorded inland as far as Bwiam. Breeds Aug–Dec.

PLOCEIDAE
Bubalornithinae

54. BUBALORNIS ALBIROSTRIS RB

Buffalo Weaver

Common resident (*B.a. albirostris*) throughout. Until 1979 found only in liddle and Upper River west to Bwiam, but since then has expanded to the coast as result of forest destruction and agricultural development. Nesting colonies, sually in Baobab trees, widely scattered in villages on both banks. Breeding season ug–Dec. Some dispersal occurs after breeding and during the dry season when ocks may be encountered anywhere.

Passerinae

55. PASSER DOMESTICUS RB

House Sparrow

Now a common breeding resident, (presumably *P.d. indicus* which is the race hich has invaded Senegal in recent years), in Banjul only. First recorded 1982–83, robably having arrived at Banjul on board a ship from Dakar where it first opeared in the 1970s.

56. PASSER GRISEUS RB

Grey-headed Sparrow

Abundant resident (*P.g. griseus*) in towns and villages throughout the country. reeding season is extended, Apr–Oct.

57. PASSER LUTEUS (DSV)

Golden Sparrow

Now an irregular dry season visitor. First reported in 1976; 7–8 (including 1 ale) on 19 Feb and 10 (including 3 males) on 24 Feb 1976 near Banjul Bund (Jensen

& Kirkeby 1980). There have been several records since: Kaur, a flock of *c.* 45 from 23–26 Mar 1981 (GOS ABR 1981), another (*c.* 200) on 25 Mar 1989 (G. Rainey), near Kuntaur, flocks of 200–400, Jan–Mar 1988 (P. Donnelly & B. Macdonald), Banjul Bund, a small flock (including one male) 16 Jan 1983 (GOS RR). An arid savanna species which occurs in Senegal and appears to be moving southwards.

468. PETRONIA (=GYMNORIS) DENTATA RI

Bush Sparrow (or Bush Petronia)

Common resident in open bush and on the borders of cultivated land in Middle and Upper River; uncommon in Lower River. Most breed during the rains Aug–Sep, but has been recorded breeding in Apr.

469. PLOCEPASSER SUPERCILIOSUS RI

(Chestnut-crowned) Sparrow-weaver

Scarce and local resident in open woodland in Lower and Middle River Recorded from Yundum, Keneba, Mansakonko and Sapu. Only breeding record Nov 1976, but presumably breeds during the rains, Jul–Nov.

470. SPOROPIPES FRONTALIS DSV

Scaly- (or Speckle-) fronted Weaver

Previously considered to be a vagrant but now appears to be a regular visitor after breeding mostly to the north bank. Until recently the only record was one observed (and photographed) in a garden at Fajara on several occasions in early Jan 1975 (GOS ABR 1975). Subsequent records are: Barra 6 on 9 Dec 1981 (GOS ABR 1981); near Essau, a party of 4–6 in late Nov each year, 1986–88 (J. N. Dymond) Serle *et al.* (1977) state that it is widespread but local in arid savanna from the desert edge southwards to about 11°N; occurs in Senegal and doubtless moving southwards with the desert.

Ploceinae

471. ANOMALOSPIZA IMBERBIS AV

Parasitic Weaver

African vagrant, only one record: a single on 24 Sep 1969 near Banjul (O Andrew in Morel 1972). Not previously known to occur north of Sierra Leone.

472. EUPLECTES AFER (=AFRA) RI

Yellow-crowned Bishop

Resident (*E.a. afer*) and locally common in freshwater swamps and ricefields Breeds Sep–Nov.

473. EUPLECTES (=COLIUSPASSER) ARDENS AV

Long-tailed Black Whydah (or Red-collared Widow-bird)

African vagrant; Bannerman (1930–51) cites one old record (*E.a. concolor* without the red collar) from The Gambia. The only other records are 2 singles, one near Karantaba and one near Bakadaji, both on 27 Aug 1963 (Cawkell 1965).

474. EUPLECTES HORDEACEUS (=HORDACEA) RB

Fire-crowned (or Black-winged Red) Bishop

Resident (*E.h. hordeaceus*) and not uncommon, on the edge of open woodland or in grassland with scattered trees, throughout the country. Breeds Aug–Nov.

475. EUPLECTES (=COLIUSPASSER) MACROURUS RB

Yellow-mantled Whydah (or Widow-bird)

A not uncommon resident (*E.m. macrourus*), confined to Lower River in swamps and ricefields. Out of the breeding season occurs in flocks of up to *c.* 40 in grassland, often away from water. Breeds Sep–Nov.

476. EUPLECTES ORIX RB

Red Bishop

Abundant resident (*E.o. franciscanus*) in open bush and grassland. When the males are in colour, Aug–Nov, they are one of the characteristic sights in open country and along the roadside. Breeds Sep–Nov, C/2–3.

[MALIMBUS NITENS

Blue-billed (or Gray's) Malimbe

Previously accepted as being an African vagrant, 4 records only: Brufut, a single bird, 2 Aug 1959 (Cawkell & Moreau); Abuko, 2 on 23 Dec 1979 (GOS ABR 1979), 2 on 28 Feb and one, possibly 2, on 21 Mar 1981 (GOS ABR 1981). Now placed in square brackets as it is likely that the records relate to *Spermophaga haematina*.]

477. MALIMBUS RUBRICEPS AV

Red-winged Malimbe

African vagrant, 3 records only: one 30 May 1969 (no location given) (Morel 1972); a male at Barra, 9 Jan 1975 (Jensen & Kirkeby 1980); and a male in open woodland near Basse, 28 Feb 1980 (GOS ABR 1980). A dry-country species locally and sparingly distributed in the savanna from The Gambia to the Central African Republic.

[MALIMBUS RUBRICOLLIS Rejected

Red-headed Malimbe

Included in square brackets in GOS Rev because the one 1975 record lacked sufficient detail. I also do not consider this acceptable for the check-list.]

478. PLOCEUS (=PLESIOSITAGRA) CUCULLATUS RB

(Black-headed) Village Weaver

Abundant resident (*P.c. cucullatus*) throughout the country; a major pest to the grain crops. Breeds colonially in tall trees, usually in the centre of villages, Aug–Nov.

479. PLOCEUS (=PLESIOSITAGRA) HEUGLINI — RB

Heuglin's Masked Weaver

Rare resident, recorded only in Lower River, from Yundum and Jabang, where several colonies of 4–6 nests were first located in 1976 in Winter Thorns *Faidherbia (Acacia) albida*, always adjacent to wasps nests. Also reported from Kiang West, and Seringmass on the north bank, where Lowe collected several specimens in 1929 (Bannerman 1930–51). Exceptionally, 34 nests on telephone wires on The Gambia/Senegal border north of Barra, Nov 1975. Breeds Jul–Nov.

480. PLOCEUS (=SITAGRA) LUTEOLUS — RB

Little Weaver

Recorded (*P.l. luteolus*) only from Lower and Middle River where it is a not uncommon and widely distributed resident in open woodland. Occurs regularly in gardens at Fajara. Pairs breed singly Jul–Nov, C/2 usual. Nest in tree at Brufut (Oct 1989) some 36 m (40 yards) from site in tree (subsequently felled) where photographed in Nov 1975 (M. E. J. Gore).

481. PLOCEUS MELANOCEPHALUS (=SITAGRA CAPITALIS) — RB

Black-headed Weaver

Abundant (*P.m. melanocephalus*) along the river bank in Middle and Upper River above the mangrove belt; particularly numerous between Sapu and Georgetown where colonies are virtually continuous in the low vegetation along the river's edge. Scarce near the coast; colonies of 5–10 nests have been reported sporadically at Abuko, Banjul Bund and Camaloo. Breeds Aug–Oct, C/2 usual.

482. PLOCEUS (=CINNAMOPTERYX CASTANEOFUSCUS) NIGERRIMUS — ?RB

Vieillot's Black (or Chestnut-and-black) Weaver

Status uncertain; possibly a rare resident. The only records are: a single female watched at Lamin, 19 May 1963, answering another, unseen, bird in a thick bush nearby (Cawkell 1965): a pair near Basse, 17 Aug 1977 (GOS ABR 1977); a small colony with nests discovered between Basse and Sutokoba, 16 Jan 1979 (A. Moore); at Pirang, 3 in May 1985 and 4 in Oct 1986 (G.G.F.P.).

483. PLOCEUS NIGRICOLLIS (=HYPHANTURGUS BRACHYPTERUS) — RB

Spectacled (or Black-necked) Weaver

Uncommon resident (*P.n. brachypterus*) in Lower and Middle River east to Baboon I. Hopkinson (Bannerman 1930–51) described it as fairly numerous but this is not the case today, doubtless because of the destruction of dense bush, which is its usual habitat. Occurs in gardens at Fajara and Yundum. Pairs breed singly, Jul–Nov.

484. PLOCEUS VELATUS (=PLESIOSITAGRA VITELLINUS) — RB

Vitelline Masked Weaver

Scarce local resident (*P.v. vitellinus*); mostly recorded in the Sudan savanna on the north bank and in Upper River. In Lower River the only report of a breeding colony was at Keneba, where *c.* 20 nests were occupied in Oct 1975; it is not known whether this colony still exists. At Sapu, in Middle River, one apparently unmated male was building in Nov 1975. (Common near the coast at Kaolack, a few kilometres north of The Gambia in Senegal.) (White reduced *P. vitellinus* to a subspecies of *P. velatus*.)

485. QUELEA ERYTHROPS RB

Red-headed Dioch (or Quelea)

Scarce, local resident in Middle River, where several flocks of up to 20 birds were seen in breeding plumage in open grassland adjoining ricefields at Sapu and Jakhaly during the rains, Jul–Nov 1974 (GOS Rev). First confirmed breeding was a colony discovered on Kai Hai I., Jul 1980 (GOS RR). Flocks of up to 50, reported in Lower River and near the coast at Camaloo and Banjul Bund in Apr, indicate a movement before the breeding season.

486. QUELEA QUELEA (DSV)

Black-faced Dioch (or Red-billed Quelea)

Today a rare and irregular visitor (*Q.q. quelea*) during the dry season. Hopkinson (Bannerman 1930–51) described it as common though Bannerman (1953) said its status was a little uncertain, and Cawkell saw it only once. Records since are: Cape St Mary, a small flock, 19 Feb 1975 (GOS ABR 1975); Camaloo, *c.* 20 on 11 Apr 1976 (GOS ABR 1976); 4 on 14 Apr 1977 (GOS ABR 1977), 2 on 14 Jan 1978 (M. E. Smalley); Banjul Bund, 3 with a large flock of *Q. erythrops*, 10 Apr 1977 (GOS ABR 1977). The only record during the wet season is 2 near Chamoi, Upper River, 27 Aug 1963; one of these was seen leaving a nest (Cawkell 1965) — doubtless a 'cock's nest', as there is no evidence of breeding.

[XANTHOPHILUS XANTHOPS Rejected

Holub's Golden Weaver

Seven or 8 olive-yellow, middle to large-sized, yellow headed weavers, accompanied by females, were watched building nests and singing in shrubs on an island at Pirang in October 1986 and were described by the observers as being most likely this species (G.G.F.P.). They placed their record in square brackets and I have decided to reject it as the nearest location to The Gambia where it occurs is Gabon. The species ranges across southern central Africa and is not known to travel far from its breeding grounds. I am inclined to the view that the birds were precocious immature *Ploceus cucullatus*, the males of which often establish small colonies and start nest building before they have achieved adult plumage.]

Viduinea

487. VIDUA CAMERUNENSIS ?

Cameroon Indigo Finch

Status uncertain; only one certain record although it may be overlooked as it is extremely difficult to separate the various species of African Indigo Finches in the field. A single male at Wallikunda, 8 Feb 1986 (GOS RR). The observer provided a detailed description including reference to the distinctive violet bill and legs.

488. VIDUA (=HYPOCHERA) CHALYBEATA RB

Senegal Indigo Finch (or Green Indigo-bird)

Common resident (*V.c. chalybeata*), widely distributed mainly in and around villages. Males in breeding plumage Jul–Jan; parasitic mainly on *Lagonosticta senegala*. Forms mixed flocks with *V. macroura* and *V. orientalis* during the dry season.

489. VIDUA MACROURA RB

Pin-tailed Whydah

Resident and widely distributed in open country, but nowhere common. Parasitic on Waxbill species; males in breeding plumage Jun–Nov. (See also under *V. chalybeata*.)

490. VIDUA (=STEGANURA) ORIENTALIS RB

Broad-tailed Paradise Whydah

Scarce resident (*V.o. aucapum*) in open country, mainly in Middle and Upper River; rare in Lower River. Parasitic, elsewhere on *Pytilia* species; presumably in The Gambia on *Pytilia phoenicoptera*. Males in breeding plumage Jul–Dec. (See also under *V. chalybeata*.)

[VIDUA WILSONI/VIDUA FUNEREA NIGERIAE

Wilson's Indigo Finch/Nigerian Indigo Finch

The records for both species (Jensen & Kirkeby 1980) must be questionable (see note on the problem of separating the Indigo Finches under *V. camerunensis*). There is a BMNH specimen of *V. funerea* labelled 'Senegambia' but this is not necessarily The Gambia and *V. wilsoni* is included in The Gambia by Serle *et al.* White gives *V. wilsoni* and *V. nigeriae* as subspecies of *V. chalybeata*. Both species were unknown to Hopkinson and to Cawkell and the GOS have no records.]

STURNIDAE
Sturninae

491. CINNYRICINCLUS LEUCOGASTER AfM, (MB?)

Amethyst (or Violet-backed) Starling

Scarce visitor (*C.l. leucogaster*) in open woodland before and during the rains. Annual numbers vary considerably; in some years not uncommon, in others few seen. Recorded Mar–Nov, most May–Jun. Breeding has never been proved, but a pair was seen entering a hole in a palm tree by Kotu Stream, Jun 1966 and another pair, with male displaying, at Howbah, May 1973 (GOS Rev); similar behaviour by 2 pairs observed at Tanji, May 1989 (C. R. Barlow).

492. CREATOPHORA CINEREA AV

Wattled Starling

African vagrant; details received (since GOS ABR 1976) from I. L. Nielson, together with a photograph, confirm the presence of 3 at Cape St Mary seen on several occasions, Jan 1976. The only record. This constitutes a considerable extension of range which is mainly East and Central Africa. It is subject to erratic movements and Serle *et al.* (1977) give its nearest occurrence as eastern Central African Republic.

493. LAMPROTORNIS CAUDATUS RB

Long-tailed Glossy Starling

Resident (*L.c. caudatus*), widely distributed and common in open country, open bush, roadsides and gardens; in some areas almost abundant. Breeds Sep–Nov.

494. LAMPROTORNIS (=LAMPROCOLIUS) CHALCURUS RB*

Short-tailed (or Bronze-tailed) Glossy Starling

Probably not uncommon (*L.c. chalcurus*) and widely distributed, but difficult to separate from *L. chalybaeus* and *L. chloropterus* in the field. Hopkinson (Bannerman 1930–51) refers only to 'Glossy Starlings' without attempting to specify. There is a significant movement of mixed flocks of Glossy Starlings (flocks of 1000+ are not unusual) through the country in Oct–Nov and recently many individuals have been positively identified as this species. Largest number recorded: *c.* 300 along the river between Bansang and Basse, 20–23 Dec 1981 (GOS ABR 1981). There are no breeding records.

495. LAMPROTORNIS (=LAMPROCOLIUS) CHALYBAEUS RB

Blue-eared Glossy Starling

Common resident (*L.c. chalybaeus*) in open bush, cleared agricultural land, gardens; the most abundant of the glossy starlings, often occurring in large numbers in mixed flocks (see under *C. chalcurus*). First breeding record: a pair (photographed) at nest-hole in hollow fence post at Yundum, May 1989; young fledged early June (R. Webzell).

496. LAMPROTORNIS (=LAMPROCOLIUS) CHLOROPTERUS RB?

Lesser Blue-eared Glossy Starling

Uncommon, probably resident (*L.c. chloropterus*) in open woodland having been recorded in most months of the year in Lower River but there are no breeding records; elsewhere in Africa breeding occurs immediately before the start of the rains. Occurs in mixed flocks (see under *C. chalcurus*) but in smaller numbers than *L. chalybaeus*.

497. LAMPROTORNIS (=LAMPROCOLIUS) PURPUREUS RB

Purple Glossy Starling

Common resident (*L.p. purpureus*), widely distributed in open bush, gardens and cleared agricultural land with scattered trees throughout the country. Breeds immediately before and during the early part of the rains, May–Jul. Small numbers often join mixed flocks (see under *C. chalcurus*).

498. LAMPROTORNIS (=LAMPROCOLIUS) SPLENDIDUS DSV

Splendid Glossy Starling

A forest species subject to local movements, recorded (*L.s. chrysonotis*) only in the dry season, Dec–Jun. Flocks up to 25 at Abuko and Fajara, Jan–Feb and 50 at

Sibanor in Mar. [There is a breeding record at Banjul, May–Jun (GOS Rev), but I consider this due to misidentification.]

499. SPREO PULCHER RB

Chestnut-bellied Starling

Local, common resident at Fajara and Bakau since the mid 1960s being confined to a 1 km stretch of the Atlantic Road at Fajara, between Pipeline Road and the Army Depot. First seen there on 29 Oct 1965 and probably breeding 1966 (I. A. McGregor); by 1980 there were *c.* 15 pairs resident. In the past 10 years, its range has extended and numbers increased elsewhere. Hopkinson (Bannerman 1930–51) found them only on the North Bank in Nuimi District inland to 65 km, but range now extends inland to Farafenni where recorded on 24 July 1978 (P. Manser) and in Jan 1986 (GOS RR). Two seen at Yundum on 15 Jan 1984 (GOS RR). Breeds towards the end of the dry season; stick nest in acacia tree contained 3 young, late Jun 1975 (M. E. J. Gore).

Buphaginae

500. BUPHAGUS AFRICANUS RB

Yellow-billed Oxpecker

Resident (*B.a. africanus*), widespread and locally common, always in company with animals, normally cattle. First breeding record: nest C/2 in hollow fence post at Yundum, Jul 1989; subsequently flooded (C. R. Barlow).

ORIOLIDAE

501. ORIOLUS AURATUS RB

African Golden Oriole

Not uncommon and widely distributed resident (*O.a. auratus*) in open woodland, occasionally in gardens. Breeds Apr–Jul, C/3.

502. ORIOLUS ORIOLUS (WV?)

(European) Golden Oriole

Status uncertain, probably an occasional Palaearctic winter visitor (*O.o. oriolus*) in open forest but overlooked because of its similarity to *O. auratus*. Budgett (1901) considered it fairly common at Kwinella, but fails to mention the resident species. Hopkinson (Bannerman 1930–51) said that a few visited The Gambia each winter and he collected one, 27 Nov 1905; the only record since is one positively identified by Cawkell at Banjul, Dec 1959 (Cawkell & Moreau).

DICRURIDAE

503. DICRURUS ADSIMILIS RB

Glossy-backed Drongo

Resident (*D.a. divaricatus*), common and widespread in open country with scattered trees, on the edge of forest and in gardens. Breeds Jun–Oct, C/2.

504. DICRURUS LUDWIGII (=SHARPEI) ?

Square-tailed Drongo

Status uncertain, probably a rare resident in remnant forest as it is common in forest in Casamance (Morel & Morel in prep.). Bannerman (1930–51) refers to a skin as *D. sharpei* in BMNH labelled 'Gambia', but expresses doubt that it occurs so far west. However, Budgett (1901) describes *D. atripennis* (=*D. ludwigii*), as being common at Niani Maru in May 1899, and there are 2 skins, one ad and one imm, taken by him in The Gambia, in the Cambridge Zoological collection. Hopkinson (Bannerman 1930–51) merely 'thought' he had seen it in the thick bush on the south bank at the end of the dry season. The only recent sightings are: Kabafitta Forest Reserve, one on 18 and 24 Dec 1975 (GOS ABR 1975); Abuko, one on 14 and 17 Dec 1979 (R. Hume, D. Fisher); Mile 65 Banjul-Soma Road, 4 in forest strip, 23 Dec 1980 (GOS ABR 1980). Two records at Kotu Stream and nearby at Bungalow Beach Hotel, Feb 1976 (Jensen & Kirkeby 1980) owing to the habitat must be considered questionable.

CORVIDAE

505. CORVUS ALBUS RB

Pied Crow

Resident, common and increasing around towns and villages near the coast, nesting in Banjul and its environs; less numerous further inland, where it appears mainly as a dry season visitor to breed Apr–Aug. After breeding disperses to the coast, where numbers increase noticeably during the rains.

506. CORVUS RUFICOLLIS AV

Brown-necked Raven

African vagrant, only 5 records: Cape St Mary, one on 15 Oct 1975, 2 from 13 Nov 1975 to early Jan 1976 (GOS ABR 1975–76), 2 on 20 Oct 1985 (GOS RR); Yundum, one on 30 Apr 1979 (GOS ABR 1979); Mandina Bah, one on 21 Nov 1988 (J. N. Dymond). The nearest known breeding locality are the Cape Verde Is.

507. PTILOSTOMUS AFER RB

Black Magpie (or Piapiac)

Resident and common, widely distributed in open country, often accompanying herds of domestic animals; particularly associated with the Rhun Palm *Borassus aethiopium*, nesting at the base of the fronds. Breeds Apr–Jul.

GAZETTEER

The following locations, which are referred to in the text, are listed under the section of The River where they are to be found.

The spellings of towns and villages are variable and those used are as in the 1st Edition. Some recent maps have slightly different spellings.

LOWER RIVER

Abuko
Albreda
Allahein River

Bakau
Bakindik
Banjul
Banni
Barra
Batabut
Batelling
Berending
Bijilo
Bijilo Islands
Bintang Bolong
Bondali
Brikama
Brufut
Brumen Bridge
Bwiam

Camaloo
Cape Lagoon
Cape St Mary

Denton Bridge
Dog Island

Essau

Fajara
Farababantang

Gunjur

Howbah

Jabang
Jambur
James Island
Jennak
Jiborah

Kabafitta Forest
Kalaji
Kartong
Keneba
Kerewan
Kiang West Nat. Park
Kotu Stream
Kwinella

Lamin

Mandina Bah
Mandinari
Marakissa

Ndemban
Niumi District
Nokunda

Pelican Island
Pirang

Salikeni
Selety
Seringmass
Sibanor
Sika
Sintet
Somita
Sukuta

Tanji
Tankular
Tendaba

Yundum

MIDDLE RIVER

Baboon Island
Bambatenda
Barokunda
Buiba

Carrol's Wharf

Elephant Island

Farafenni
Fulabantang

Georgetown

Ida

Jakhaly
Jappeni
Jassong

Kaiaff
Kai Hai Island
Kaur
Karantaba
Kolior
Kudang
Kuntaur

Mansakonko
Medina

Nema
Niamina
Niani Maru
Nianija Bolong

Pakali Ba
Pakalinding

Sambang
Sankulakunda
Sapu
Sofanyama
Soma

Toniataba

Wallikunda

Yellitenda
Yoroberikunda

UPPER RIVER

Bakadaji
Bansang
Baratenda
Basse

Chamoi

Darsilami

Diabugu

Fatatenda
Fatoto

Koina

MacCarthy Island

Sabi
Sami
Sutokoba

THE GAMBIA ORNITHOLOGICAL SOCIETY'S RARE BIRD REPORT FORM

Name of observer: . . . .

This form is intended to assist you in supplying information needed to substantiate a reported sighting of a bird heretofore considered rare, vagrant or absent in The Gambia. In filling in the form, please use a bird guide for names only; give the description, behaviour, ecology, etc. from memory or from your own field notes. If the information given is other than first-hand, please so indicate. Do not be afraid to submit a form that is largely blank. Some species may be identified positively on the basis of a single field mark.

Species: . . . . (. . . . .)

(English name) (Latin name)

CIRCUMSTANCES

Date seen: . . / . . . . / . . Time of day: . . . .

Location: . . . .

Habitat details: . . . .

Your position (boat, car, on foot, etc.): . . . .

. . . .

Weather conditions: . . . .

Light (intensity, and specially direction *vis-a-vis* the observer)

. . . .

Distance to bird: . . . . metres. Optical aids: . . . .

Angle/attitude (below, eye level, above, back-to, facing, etc.)

. . . .

Duration of observation: . . . .

DESCRIPTION

Age/sex/plumage: . . . .

. . . .

Field marks (include, if seen, colours of beak, legs, eye; tail length; special features):

. . . .

. . . .

. . . .

. . . .

Behaviour: . . . .

. . . .

. . . .

. . . .

. . . .

. . . .

OTHER DETAILS

Names of other observers who saw the bird:

1. . . . .

2. . . . .

3. . . . .

Will they be submitting reports? . . . .

Did you (or others) take useable photographs? . . . .

(If so, a copy would greatly add to our records)

Any other pertinent information: . . . .

. . . .

. . . .

Observer's address: . . . .

. . . .

. . . .

. . . .

Please send to: The Recorder, G.O.S.,
P.O. Box 757, Banjul, The Gambia.

REFERENCES

ALEXANDER, W. B. 1954. *Birds of the Ocean*. 2nd Edn. Putnam, New York.

BANNERMAN, D. A. 1930–51. *Birds of Tropical Africa*. 8 vols. Oliver & Boyd, Edinburgh & London.

——— 1953. *The Birds of West and Equatorial Africa*. 2 vols. Oliver & Boyd, Edinburgh & London.

——— 1958. *Larger Birds of West Africa*. Penguin, London.

BATTEN, I. A. 1975. Lesser Crested Terns in The Gambia. *Bull. Brit. Orn. Cl.* 95: 127–128.

BENSON, C. W. & BENSON, F. M. 1977. *Birds of Malawi*. Montfort Press, Limbe.

BOURNE, W. R. P. 1963. The documentation of unusual records published in *Ibis*. *Ibis* 105: 407.

BRAY, D., MULHOLLAND, J. R. & VITTERY, A. 1966. *Notes on the Birds of The Gambia*. Duplicated, Bathurst.

BRITTON, P. L. (ed.). 1980. *Birds of East Africa*, East African Natural History Society, Nairobi.

BROWN, L. H., FRY, C. H., KEITH, S., NEWMAN, K. & URBAN, E. K., (joint eds). 1982–88. *The Birds of Africa*. 3 vols. Academic Press, London.

BROWN, L. 1970. *African Birds of Prey*. Collins, London.

BROWN, L. & AMADON, D. 1968. *Eagles, Hawks and Owls of the World*. Hamlyn, Feltham.

BROWN, R. G. B. 1979. Seabirds of the Senegal upwelling and adjacent waters. *Ibis* 121: 283–292.

BRUGGERS, R. L. & BORTOLI, L. 1979. Notes on breeding, parasitism and association with wasps of Heuglin's Weaver nesting on telephone wires in Mali. [Includes records from The Gambia.] *Malimbus* 1: 135–144.

BUDGETT, J. S. 1901. On the ornithology of The Gambia River. *Ibis* 8: 481–497.

CAWKELL, E. M. 1960. Notes from The Gambia. *Ibis* 102: 136–137.

——— 1964. The utilization of mangrove by African birds. *Ibis* 106: 251–253.

——— 1965. Notes on Gambian birds. *Ibis* 107: 535–540.

CAWKELL, E. M. & MOREAU, R. E. 1963. Notes on the birds of The Gambia. *Ibis* 105: 156–178.

CHAPMAN, E. A. 1969. Gambian observations winter 1946–47. *Bull. Brit. Orn. Cl.* 89: 96.

CHAPPUIS, C. 1974. Illustration sonore de problèmes bioacoustiques posés par les oiseaux de la zone éthiopienne. *Alauda* 42: 467–500.

CHAPPUIS, C., ERARD, C. & MOREL, G. J. 1988. Morphology, habitat, vocalisations & distributions of the River Prinia *Prinia fluviatilis*. Proc. Pan-African Ornithological Congress, Nairobi.

COLLAR, N. J. & STUART, S. N. 1985. *Threatened Birds of Africa and Related Islands* Part I. ICBP/IUCN, Cambridge.

CRAMP, S. & SIMMONS, K. E. L. (eds). 1977–88. *Handbook of the Birds of Europe, the Middle East and North Africa: The Birds of the Western Palearctic*. Vols 1–5, Oxford University Press.

DEKEYSER, P. L. 1956, 1961. Le Parc National du Niokolo-Koba: Oiseaux. *Mem. Inst. Franc. Afr. Noire* 48: 79–141; 62: 363–378.

DEKEYSER, P. G. & DERIVOT, J. H. 1966/67. *Les Oiseaux de l'Ouest Africain*, 2 vols I.F.A.N. University of Dakar, Senegal.

DUNSMORE, J. R., RAINS, A. B. & LOWE, G. D. N. 1975. *The Land Resources of The Gambia and their Development*. Ministry of Overseas Development: London.

ELGOOD, J. H. 1960. *Birds of West African Town and Garden*. Longmans, London.

——— 1982. *The Birds of Nigeria*. British Ornithologists' Union, Check-list No. 4.

ELGOOD, J. H., FRY, C. H. & DOWSETT, R. J. 1973. African migrants in Nigeria. *Ibis* 115: 1–45, 375–411.

ERARD, C., GUILLOU, J. J. & MAYAND, N. 1984. Sur l'identité specifique de certains Laridés nicheurs au Sénégal. *Alauda* 52(3), 184–188.

ERICSSON, STEFAN 1989. Notes on Birds observed in Gambia and Senegal in November 1984. *Malimbus* 11: 88–94.

FAIRBAIRN, W. A. 1952. *Some Game Birds of West Africa*. Oliver & Boyd, London.

FIELD, G. D. 1974. Nearctic Waders in Sierra Leone — Lesser Golden Plover and Buff-breasted Sandpiper. *Bull. Brit. Orn. Cl.* 94: 76–78.

FITZGERALD, W. 1964. *Africa*. Methuen, London.

FORSHAW, J. M. 1973. *Parrots of the World*. Landsdowne Press, Melbourne.

FRY, C. H. 1969. The evolution and systematics of bee-eaters (*Meropidae*). *Ibis* 111: 557–592.

——— 1980. The origin of Afrotropical kingfishers. *Ibis* 122: 57–74.

——— 1984. *The Bee-eaters*. Poyser, Calton.

GAMBIA ORNITHOLOGICAL SOCIETY (The) 1975. *Notes on the Birds of The Gambia*. Duplicated, Banjul.

——— 1976. *First Bird Report 1975*. Duplicated, Banjul.

——— 1977. *Second Bird Report 1976*. Duplicated Banjul.

——— 1978. *Third Bird Report 1977*. Duplicated, Banjul.

——— 1974–80. Newsletters 1–27. Duplicated, Banjul.

——— 1979. *Fourth Bird Report 1978*. Duplicated, Banjul.

——— 1980. *Fifth Bird Report 1979*. Duplicated, Banjul.

——— 1981. *Sixth Bird Report 1980*. Duplicated, Banjul.

——— 1983. *Seventh Bird Report 1981*. Duplicated, Banjul.

——— 1986. *Rare Birds Report 1982–86*. Banjul.

——— 1988. *Annual Bird Report 1986–87*. Banjul.

GAMBIAN–GERMAN FORESTRY PROJECT (The) 1988. *Pirang Ecological Investigations in a Forest Island in The Gambia*, Hamburg.

GEESON, J. & GEESON, J. 1990. First Red Kite record for the Gambia. *Malimbus* 11: 144.

GOODWIN, D. 1967. *Pigeons and Doves of the World*. B.M.N.H., London.

GORE, G. 1964. *Birds of The Gambia: List of 100 commonest birds*. Government Printer, Bathurst.

GORE, G. & GORE, P. 1966. The Avocet *Recurvirostra avosetta* in Senegambia. *Ibis* 108: 281.

GORE, M. E. J. 1976, 1984. *Field Check-list of the Birds of The Gambia*. G.O.S., Banjul.

——— 1980. Millions of Turtle Doves. *Malimbus* 2: 78.

GRIMES, L. G. 1987. *The Birds of Ghana*. British Ornithologists' Union, Check-list No. 9.

HALL, B. P. & MOREAU, R. E. 1970. *An Atlas of Speciation in African Passerine Birds*. B.M.N.H., London.

HANCOCK, J. A. & LLIOTT, H. F. I. 1978. *Herons of the World*. London Editions, London.

HOPKINSON, E. 1908–9. The birds of The Gambia. *Avicult., Mag*. 8 & New Series 1.

——— 1912a. The Birds of The Gambia *in* Reeve, H. F. *The Gambia*. London; reprinted 1969, Negro University Press, New York.

——— 1912b. *Bird Notes*. Avian Press, London.

——— 1916–17. Birds of The Gambia. *J. African Society* 16: 297–305.

——— 1919. *A List of the Birds of The Gambia*. Brighton.

——— 1929. Birds of The Gambia. *Elder Dempster Magazine* 7: 129–132.

——— 1923. The game birds and pigeons of The Gambia. *Avicult. Mag*. Jun–Oct: 125–131, 166–172, 183–187, 207–215, 231–237.

——— 1936. The ducks of The Gambia. *J. Royal African Society* 35: 38–52.

HUMPHREY-SMITH, G. 1954. *List of 100 Commonest Gambian Birds*. Duplicated, Bathurst.

HUTCHINSON, J. & DALZIEL, J. M. 1927. *Flora of West Tropical Africa*. 2 vols. Crown Agents, London.

JENSEN, J. V. & KIRKEBY, K. 1980. *The Birds of The Gambia*. Aros Nature Guides, Aarhus.

JENSEN, J. V. & KIRKEBY, K./GORE, M. E. J. 1987. Records of Rock Thrust *Monticola saxatilis* in The Gambia, *Malimbus* 9: 123–124.

LOWE, W. 1929. Notes on nesting and plumages of Vultures [incl. notes from The Gambia]. *Ibis* 71: 439–442.

LYNES, H. 1930. Review of the genus *Cisticola*. 2 vols. *Ibis* Suppl: 1–163.

McGREGOR, I. A. & THOMSON, A. LANDSBOROUGH. 1965. Blue Rock Thrush in The Gambia. *Ibis* 107: 401.

MACWORTH-PRAED, C. W. & GRANT, C. H. B. 1970–73. *African Handbook of Birds*. Series 3: *Birds of West Central and Western Africa*. 2 vols. Longmans, London.

MOORE, A. 1983. On Nesting of the Lavender Fire-Finch *Malimbus* 5: 56.

MOREAU, R. E. 1961. Problems of Mediterranean–Saharan Migration. *Ibis* 103a: 373–427.

——— 1966. *The Bird Faunas of Africa and its Islands*. Academic Press, London.

——— 1972. *The Palaearctic–African Bird Migration Systems.* Academic Press, London.

MOREL, G. J. 1972. *Liste Commentée des Oiseaux du Sénégal et de la Gambie.* O.R.S.T.O.M., Dakar.

——— 1973. The Sahel zone as an environment for Palaearctic migrants. *Ibis* 115: 413.

——— 1980. *Liste commentée des oiseaux du Sénégal et de la Gambie* (1972). Suppl, No. 1. Duplicated. O.R.S.T.O.M., Dakar.

MOREL, G. J. & MOREL, Y. 1959. Dates de reproduction de quelques oiseaux du Sahel senegalais. *Ostrich* Suppl 3: 260–263.

——— 1979. La Tourterelle des Bois dans l'Extreme Ouest-Africain. *Malimbus* 1: 66–67.

——— 1982. Dates de reproduction des oiseaux de Sénégambie. *Bonn. Zool. Beitr.* 33: 249–268.

——— (in prep.). *Les Oiseaux de Sénégambie (avec cartes de distribution).*

MOREL, G. J., MONNET, CLAUDE & ROUCHOUSE, CHARLES. 1983. Donnees Nouvelles sur *Monticola solitaria* et *Monticola saxatilis* en Sénégambie. *Malimbus* 5: 1–4.

MOREL, G. J. & ROUX, F. 1966. Les Migrateurs Paléarctiques au Sénégal. *Terre et Vie* 1-1966: 19–72, 2-1966: 143–176.

MORONY, J. J., BOCK, W. J. & FARRAND, J. 1975. Reference List of the Birds of the World. *Am. Mus. Nat. Hist.* New York.

NAUROIS, R. DE 1962. Faits nouveaux concernant l'époque et la durée du cycle de réproduction chez les Oiseaux d'Afrique tropicale. *C.R. Acad. Sc. Paris.* 255: 1521–1522.

——— 1965a. Les Mangroves d'Avicennia les plus septentrionales de la côte occidentale d'Afrique. *Bull. Inst. Fr. Afr. Noire.* 27, sér A, 3: 843–854.

——— 1965b. Une Colonie Reproductrice du Petit Flamant Rose dans l'Aftout es Sahel (Sud-ouest Mauritanien). *Alauda* 33, 3: 166–176.

——— 1965c. L'Avifaune aquatique du delta du Sénégal et son destin. *Bull. Inst. Fr. Afr. Noire.* 27, sér A, 3: 1196–1207.

——— 1965d. Premières récherches sur la faunistique et l'Écologie des Palmipèdes et Échassiers en Guinée portugaise: régions littorales et archipel des Bijagos. *C.R. Acad. Sc. Paris* 261: 1423–1426.

——— 1966. Colonies Reproductrices de Spatules africaines, Ibis sacrés et Laridés dans l'Archipel des Bijagos (Guinée portugaise). *Alauda* 34, 4. 1966: 257–278.

——— 1967. L'Avifaune de la côte de l'Aguerguer et de l'Ælot Virginia (Sahara espagnol, Mauritanie). *Bull. Inst. Fr. Afr. Noire.* 29, sér A, 2, 1967: 1–23.

——— 1969. Peuplement et cycles de réproduction des oiseaux de la côte Occidentale d'Afrique (du Cap Barbas, Sahara Espagnol à la République de Guinée). *Mém. Mus. Nat. Hist. Paris.*

NEUMANN, O. 1917. Uber die Avifauna des unteren Senegal-Gebieta. *J. Orn.* 65: 189–214.

NIELSON, B. P. 1975. Lesser Crested Terns *Sterna bengalensis* in Gambia. *Bull. Brit. Orn. Cl.* 95: 80–81.

OGILBY, W. 1835. Descriptions of mammals and birds of The Gambia. *Proc. Zool. Soc. Lond.*

REICHENOW, A. 1900–04. *Die Vogel Afrikas.* 3 vols. Neudamm.

RENDALL, P. 1892. Notes on the ornithology of The Gambia. *Ibis* (6)4: 215–230.

ROCHEBRUNE, A. T. DE 1886. *Faune de la Sénégambie: Oiseaux.* Paris.

ROUX, F. 1959a. Quelques données sur les Anatidés et Charadriidés paléarctic hivernant dans la basse vallée du Sénégal et sur leur écologie. *Terre et Vie* 106: 315–321.

——— 1959b. Capture des migrateurs paléarctiques dans la basse vallée du Sénégal. *Bull. Mus. Nat. Hist. Paris* (2) 31: 335–340.

SERLE, W., MOREL, G. J. & HARTWIG, W. 1977. *A Field Guide to the Birds of West Africa.* Collins, London.

SHELLEY, G. E. 1887. *In* Maloney, A. *Sketch of the Forestry of West Africa: Birds.* pp. 464–483.

SIMS, T. & ANDREWS, O. 1969. *Birds of The Gambia: The Second Hundred.* Government Printer, Bathurst.

SMALLEY, M. E. 1979. Dowitcher in The Gambia. *Malimbus* 1: 68.

——— 1979a. Cattle Egrets feeding on flies attracted to mangoes. *Malimbus* 1: 114–117.

——— 1983a. The Marsh Owl *Asio capensis*: a Wet Season Migrant to The Gambia. *Malimbus* 5: 31–33.

——— 1983b. Abyssinian Rollers *Coracias abyssinica* and European Rollers *C. garrulus* in The Gambia, *Malimbus* 5: 34–36.

SMITH, K. D. 1965. On the Birds of Morocco. *Ibis* 107: 452–492.

SNOW, D. W. (ed.). 1978. *An Atlas of Speciation in African Non-Passerine Birds*. B.M.N.H., London.

——— 1979. Atlas of Speciation in African Non-Passerine Birds — *Addenda* and *Corrigenda*. *Bull. Brit. Orn. Cl.* 99: 66–68.

SNOW, D. W. & LOUETTE, M. 1981. Atlas of Speciation in African Non-Passerine Birds — *Addenda* and *Corrigenda 2, Bull. Brit, Orn. Cl.* 101: 336–339.

SWAINSON, W. 1837–43. *The Natural History of the Birds of Western Africa*. The Naturalists' Library. Ornithology Vols VII–VIII: 286 and 263. Edinburgh.

THIOLLAY, J.-M. 1985. The Birds of the Ivory Coast. *Malimbus* 7: 1–59.

THOMSON, A. LANDSBOROUGH. 1964. *A New Dictionary of Birds*. Nelson, London & New York.

——— 1966. The status of two swallow species in The Gambia. *Ibis* 108: 281.

VAURIE, C. 1959. *The Birds of the Palearctic Fauna*. 2 vols. Witherby, London.

VIETINGHOFF-RIESCH, A. 1955. *Die Rauchschwalbe*. Duncker & Humblot, Berlin.

WHITE, C. M. N. 1961, 1962, 1963. *A Revised Check-list of African Passerine Birds*. Govt. of Zambia, Lusaka.

——— 1965. *A Revised Check-list of African Non-Passerine Birds*. Govt. of Zambia, Lusaka.

WILLIAMS, J. G. 1963. *A Field Guide to the Birds of East and Central Africa*. Collins, London.

WITHERBY, H. F., JOURDAIN, F. C. R., TICEHURST, N. F. & TUCKER, B. W. 1938–41. *The Handbook of British Birds*. 5 vols. Witherby, London.

INDEX OF SCIENTIFIC NAMES

FAMILIES

GENERA AND SPECIES

INDEX OF ENGLISH NAMES